Little Duck's First Christmas

Some other books to enjoy:

Duck's Easter Egg Hunt

Written by Dawn Richards,
illustrated by Heidi D'hamers

Mole's Harvest Moon

Mouse's Christmas Wish

By Judi Abbot

LITTLE DUCK'S FIRST CHRISTMAS
A PICTURE CORGI BOOK
978 0 552 57468 6
First published in Great Britain by Picture Corgi,
an imprint of Random House Children's Publishers UK
A Random House Group Company
This edition published 2012
9 7 5 3 2 4 6 8 10

Picture Corgi Books are published by Random House Children's Publishers UK, 61-63 Uxbridge Road, London W5 5SA
www.kidsatrandomhouse.co.uk
www.randomhouse.co.uk
Addresses for companies within The Random House Group Limited can be found at: www.randomhouse.co.uk/offices.htm
THE RANDOM HOUSE GROUP Limited Reg. No. 954009
A CIP catalogue record for this book is available from the British Library.
Printed in China

Little Duck's First Christmas

Dawn Richards & Heidi D'hamers

Picture Corgi

It was the day before Christmas. Snow was falling gently in the village, as everyone helped with the final preparations.

The Hedgehog family had made some mince pies.

The Mole family sang Christmas carols.

The Cat and Rabbit families were decorating the huge Christmas tree.

And the Duck family . . .

Well, the Duck family felt particularly excited – it was Little Duck's first ever Christmas.

"Will the Christmas Bear come and give me lots of presents?" Little Duck asked anxiously.

"Of course," quacked Mummy Duck with a smile. "You've been a very good little duck all year, so don't you worry."

But Little Duck did worry. "Am I really a good little duck?" she wondered. "Am I good enough for the Christmas Bear to come?" She couldn't think of one very good thing that she'd done.

"I know something really good I can do," said Little Duck to herself.

"I'll go to the Christmas market and get Mummy and Daddy a special present to open on Christmas morning."

Pleased with her good idea, Little Duck wrapped herself up warmly and set off for the Christmas market. It was open all day, so she would have lots of time to choose the perfect gift.

But as she was walking along the road – **WHOMP!**
Little Duck felt something cold hit her on the back.
"Ooof!" said Little Duck. "What was that?"

"Gotcha," said Caspar Cat, and he bent down to pick up another snowball. Little Duck was about to get cross, when she saw a snowball flying towards Casper Cat.

WHACK went the snowball as it landed right on his head. "Ha ha!" laughed Mary Mole. Casper did look funny.

Soon Little Duck was deep in the middle of a snowball fight with her friends.

"Now let's build a snow mountain," called Mary.

"That is a really **good** snow mountain," said Casper, feeling satisfied.

"**Good!**" thought Little Duck, suddenly remembering.

"I'm not being a **good** little duck at all – the Christmas Bear will never come!" and with that she hurried on towards the market.

As Little Duck waddled on her way, she suddenly heard a . . .

What could it be?

It was her friends Harry Hedgehog and Ben Badger.
"Come and have a go on our sled," they cried.

Soon Little Duck was whizzing down the hill.

"This hill's all right," said Ben Badger. "But I know a really **good** hill for sledding."
"**Good!**" thought Little Duck as she remembered her plan.

"I'm not being a **good** little duck at all – the Christmas Bear will never come!" And she left her friends and sped on towards the market.

But as she hurried along she stumbled across Sammy Goose.
"What are you doing lying in the snow?" asked Little Duck.
"I'm making snow angels," said Sammy Goose. "It's fun!"

So Little Duck helped Sammy Goose make shapes in the snow.
"Look," said Sammy breathlessly. "We've made ten **good** little angels."

"**Good!**" thought Little Duck - she had forgotten again . . . "I'm being a very **bad** little duck - the Christmas Bear will never come!"

And she quickly brushed herself down and rushed on towards the market.

But when Little Duck reached the Christmas market, it had already closed.

Oh no, Little Duck!

Little Duck walked home sadly along the snowy path and past the frozen lake. By the lake she saw Dog, busy making beautiful ice sculptures.

When Little Duck explained what had happened, Dog gave her a lovely little ice duck. The perfect gift for Mummy and Daddy Duck.

Little Duck carefully put the ice duck in her pocket and then hurried home, as it was getting very late.
"Where have you been?" quacked Mummy and Daddy Duck when Little Duck arrived home. "We were so worried."

"I've been a very good little duck. And I have a surprise for you."

But when Little Duck reached into her pocket to put the ice duck under the tree, all she found was a puddle of water. The little ice duck had melted all away.

Little Duck was miserable. She crept into bed and sobbed quietly to herself. The Christmas Bear would never come, and neither she nor her parents would have any presents on Christmas morning.

Finally Little Duck fell asleep, but in the middle of the night she awoke to a strange sound. She crept down to the living room to see what it could be . . .

It was the **Christmas Bear!**

"But I haven't been good," whispered Little Duck.
"You've had a very good try," laughed the Christmas Bear,
"and that's what counts."

The room was full of magic as the Christmas Bear placed present after present under the tree.

"Now, don't open them until morning," he said with a wink. Then, with a shimmer of magic, he disappeared.

The next morning, Little Duck opened her presents in a flutter and a flap of excitement. She had lots of toys and sweets from the Christmas Bear and some special treats from her mum and dad.

"But I don't have a present for you," said Little Duck sadly.
"Oh, we don't need a present," said Mummy and Daddy Duck, giving each other a big smile.

"And maybe we can help play with your presents," laughed Daddy Duck.

Later that morning the Duck family went out into the village to say Merry Christmas to all their friends.

"What did you get for Christmas?" Cat asked Mummy Duck.

"We shared a wonderful Christmas cuddle," said Mummy Duck.

The best present of all!

Work effectively in accounting

Tutorial

Michael Fardon
Roger Petheram

Published by Osborne Books Limited
Unit 1B Everoak Estate
Bromyard Road
Worcester WR2 5HP
Tel 01905 748071
Email books@osbornebooks.co.uk
Website www.osbornebooks.co.uk

Design by Laura Ingham
Cover and page design image © Istockphoto.com/Petrovich9

Printed and bound by CPI Group (UK) Ltd, Croydon, CR0 4YY

British Library Cataloguing in Publication Data
A catalogue record for this book is available from the British Library

ISBN 978 1905777 273

Contents

Acknowledgements

The publisher wishes to thank the following for their help with the reading and production of the book: Maz Loton and Jon Moore. Thanks are also due to Laura Ingham for her designs for this series.

The publisher is indebted to the Association of Accounting Technicians for its help and advice to our authors and editors during the preparation of this text.

Authors

Michael Fardon has extensive teaching experience of a wide range of banking, business and accountancy courses at Worcester College of Technology. He now specialises in writing business and financial texts and is General Editor at Osborne Books. He is also an educational consultant and has worked extensively in the areas of vocational business curriculum development.

Roger Petheram has lectured at Worcester College of Technology on a wide range of accounting, business and management courses for a number of years. He previously worked as a senior accountant for the Health Service. He is currently senior editor for accounting texts at Osborne Books, with particular responsibility for the AAT Series.

Introduction

what this book covers

This book has been written specifically to cover the Learning Area 'Work effectively in Accounting and Finance' which covers a single QCF Unit in the AAT Level 2 Certificate in Accounting:

- Work Effectively in Accounting and Finance

The book contains a clear text with worked examples and case studies, chapter summaries and key terms to help with revision. Each chapter has a wide range of student activities.

International Accounting Standards (IAS) terminology

In this book the appropriate accounting terms are quoted when they first appear in a chapter as follows: IAS terminology (UK terminology), for example: 'inventory (stock).' On subsequent occasions in the chapter the international term may be quoted on its own, eg 'inventory.'

Changes in assessment - new material from Osborne Books

At the time of writing AAT had announced that assessment of this Learning Area was to be changed to a Computer Based Test, due to come into effect from 1 October 2012. In view of the change of method of assessment, the AAT sample project and answers have been removed from this text.

To find out about new practice assessment material for this Learning Area please visit the website www.osbornebooks.co.uk for further details.

1 Accounting and finance in the workplace

this chapter covers...

This chapter is an introduction to the role played by the accounting function in the workplace; it shows how accounting 'works' in an organisation such as a business. It describes the various areas in which accounting and finance staff are likely to work and the way in which the size of the organisation will affect job roles and working relationships.

The chapter explains the following:

- *the difference between book-keeping and accounting – book-keeping involves the keeping of financial records and accounting involves the processing and reporting of this financial information*
- *accounting has a number of important roles within a business, including recording financial information, financial reporting, forecasting, planning and managing*
- *financial accounting deals with external reporting of past events, whereas management accounting deals with internal financial forecasting and planning*
- *basic accounting carried out by book-keepers and accounts assistants involves a wide variety of areas – sales order processing, purchasing, cashiering, payroll, costing and stock control*
- *in larger organisations the basic accounting staff report to financial and management accounting managers and auditors along defined reporting lines*
- *an effective working environment will have efficient reporting lines*

ACCOUNTING AND FINANCE FUNCTIONS

accounting and finance

The terms 'accounting' and 'finance' are sometimes used loosely to relate to 'dealing with money', but it is important to be able to distinguish between the two and identify the functions they fulfil in an organisation.

It is easier to start with finance because it has a more restricted meaning:

Finance involves providing and managing funds and resources for an organisation such as a business.

If you work in a 'finance' company you are likely to lend money or provide products such as hire purchase. If you work in a finance department you are likely to be involved in managing money and other resources.

Accounting, on the other hand, involves rather more than this:

Accounting is a system for recording, analysing and reporting financial transactions and the financial status of a business.

Accounting is based on finance, but it takes things further, analysing and reporting financial data.

accounting – the oldest profession in the world?

Accounting has sometimes been described as one of the oldest professions in the world. The word **accounting** involves a number of concepts which have been in use since the Egyptian Pharoahs built the pyramids:

- keeping financial records – 'accounts' – of money spent and money received in relation to a project or a business
- using this information to 'account' to people who have interest in the project or business, for example the owners or the people providing the money – giving estimates of income, spending (expenses), making a profit or a loss, calculating money owed and money due

a note on keeping records – book-keeping

The task of keeping records of financial transactions such as income and expenses forms the 'nuts and bolts' of accounting. Traditionally known as book-keeping, it developed over six hundred years ago in Italy into a double-entry system which involved every transaction being recorded in two separate 'accounts'. **Book-keeping**, therefore, is the process of keeping financial records; **accounting**, on the other hand, takes the process further, analysing and reporting this information to business owners and other people who are interested in the business, the stakeholders. These 'stakeholders' include the public, the government, lenders, customers and suppliers.

present-day functions of accounting

In order to act in the interests of the business and its stakeholders, accounting staff have to carry out a wide range of functions, including:

- **recording and reporting**

  recording data and preparing financial reports about what has happened in the past – sales figures, income statements, tax calculations, VAT returns

- **forecasting**

  preparing financial forecasts and budgets – these are estimates of what is expected to happen in the future

- **monitoring and control**

  comparing the figures in forecasts and budgets with what actually happens and then taking corrective action if the figures are off target

- **external auditing**

  checking by external and independent accountants that the recording of financial transactions within the organisation is accurate and in accordance with rules laid down by external regulatory bodies

- **internal auditing**

  checking by the organisation's own staff that the recording of financial transactions is accurate and in accordance with internal rules

In short, accounting is concerned with

- **recording** financial data
- **reporting** financial data
- **planning** for the organisation's future – setting objectives and targets
- **managing** the organisation – taking action if the targets are not met

financial and management accounting

Accounting is traditionally divided into two types – financial accounting and management accounting:

- **financial accounting** is involved with financial transactions that have already happened and with the preparation and interpretation of financial statements for the benefit of managers, the owners and in some cases the external stakeholders of an organisation

- **management accounting** deals with all aspects of providing financial data to management (eg future income and costs) so that planning can take place and decisions made, eg reducing or increasing selling prices or switching resources from one product or service to another

ACCOUNTING ROLES

In this section we look at the different roles carried out by people working in accounting jobs. It must be appreciated that there are many different types of organisation that carry out accounting processes: some large, many small, some state-owned or controlled and many privately owned.

Whatever the organisation, the accounting function must still take place. Generally speaking the larger the organisation, the greater the need for control and accountability to outside stakeholders. In a smaller business – a sole trader local taxi service, for example – the accounting records are far less complex and the owner only accountable to himself/herself and to the tax authorities.

basic accounting roles

Anyone can keep the 'books' of a business; the important point is that they must be kept accurately – by the owner, or by a full or part-time book-keeper or accounts assistant employed for the purpose. Book-keepers do not have to be qualified, although it is better if they are. The basic accounting roles can be performed by someone coming in for a day a week to write up the books of a small business, or by hundreds of accounting staff employed by the accounts departments of larger companies. The books may be hand-written, or computerised, although larger businesses invariably use computers.

In a small business the book-keeper or accounts assistant is likely to carry out a wide variety of tasks (see diagram on the next page), for example:

- **sales order processing**: taking sales orders, producing invoices, monitoring receipts – all the jobs connected with the sales ledger
- **purchasing**: sending out orders, checking the incoming documentation, making payments – all the jobs connected with the purchases ledger
- **cashiering** – recording incoming and outgoing payments and dealing with cash held in the business – all the jobs connected with the cash book or the petty cash book
- **payroll** – maintaining payroll records, calculating the payroll and processing payroll payments

Other specialist accounting jobs include:

- **costing** – working out the figures for the cost of products and services and preparing reports for management
- **inventory (stock) control** – monitoring and re-ordering inventory

In a larger business, because of the volume of transactions, these jobs are likely to be departmentalised; employees are likely to remain in one specialist accounting area and gain expertise there.

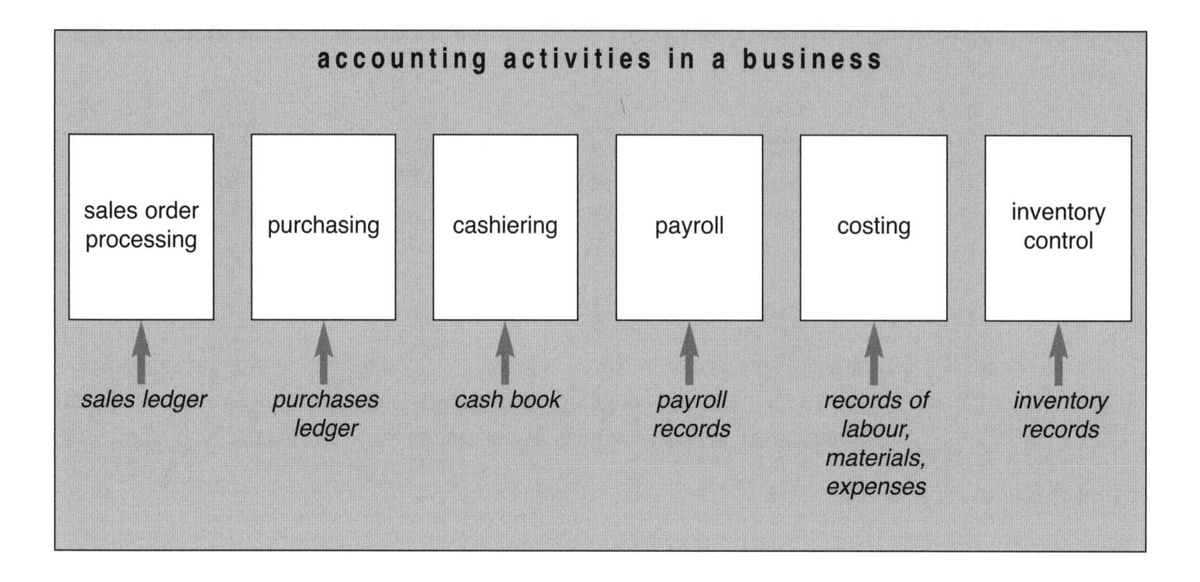

accountants in the organisation

The role of the **accountant** – who should be professionally qualified – is to check, summarise, present, analyse and interpret the accounts for the benefit of the owner/owners and other interested parties. In larger organisations accountants form the next level up from the accounts assistants. They may be:

- line managers, supervising the work of the accounts assistants
- senior managers, taking responsibility for specific functional areas

There are three main types of specialist accountant:

- **financial accountants**, who deal with internal and external reporting
- **management accountants**, who deal with reporting and budgeting
- **auditors**, who check that the accounting procedures have been carried out correctly

financial accountant

The function of the **financial accountant** is very much concerned with financial transactions, and with using the information produced by the book-keeper or accounts assistant. The financial accountant extracts information from the accounting records in order to provide a method of control, for example, over customers who buy on credit, over suppliers, cash and bank balances.

The role of a financial accountant also involves the periodic analysis and reporting of financial data so that financial statements – such as the income statement and the statement of financial position – can be prepared for internal use and also for external use.

management accountant

The **management accountant** obtains information about costs – eg the cost of labour, materials, expenses (overheads) – and interprets the data and prepares reports and budgets for the owners or managers of the business. In particular, the management accountant is concerned with financial decision-making, planning and control of the business.

auditors

Auditors are accountants whose role is to check that accounting procedures have been followed correctly. There are two types of auditors: external auditors and internal auditors.

External auditors are independent of the business whose accounts are being audited. They are normally members of firms of accountants. The most common type of audit conducted by external auditors is the audit of larger limited companies required by law. In this situation, the auditors are reporting to the shareholders of a company, stating that the legal requirements laid down in the Companies Acts have been complied with, and that the accounts represent a 'true and fair view' of the state of the business.

Internal auditors are employed or contracted by the business which they audit. Their duties are concerned with the internal check and control procedures of the business, for example monitoring the procedures for the control of cash, and the authorisation of purchases. The nature of their work requires that they should have a degree of independence within the company.

HOW ACCOUNTING SUPPORTS THE ORGANISATION

The accounting function in an organisation fulfils an important support role to the other functions in the organisation. The accounting function can provide the other departments with information about the financial implications of their activities. For example:

- the sales ledger section can keep sales representatives updated with the credit status of their customers, highlighting any slow payers
- the purchases ledger section can advise the Administration Department of how much is owed to suppliers for purchases and overhead expenses
- the payroll section can advise the Human Resources Department about payroll costs, for example how much overtime was paid last month
- the costing section can advise the Production Department on the direct costs of production (eg materials) and also the overhead costs of production
- the cashier handles and records the cash sales for the Sales Department

This support of the organisation by the accounting functions is shown below:

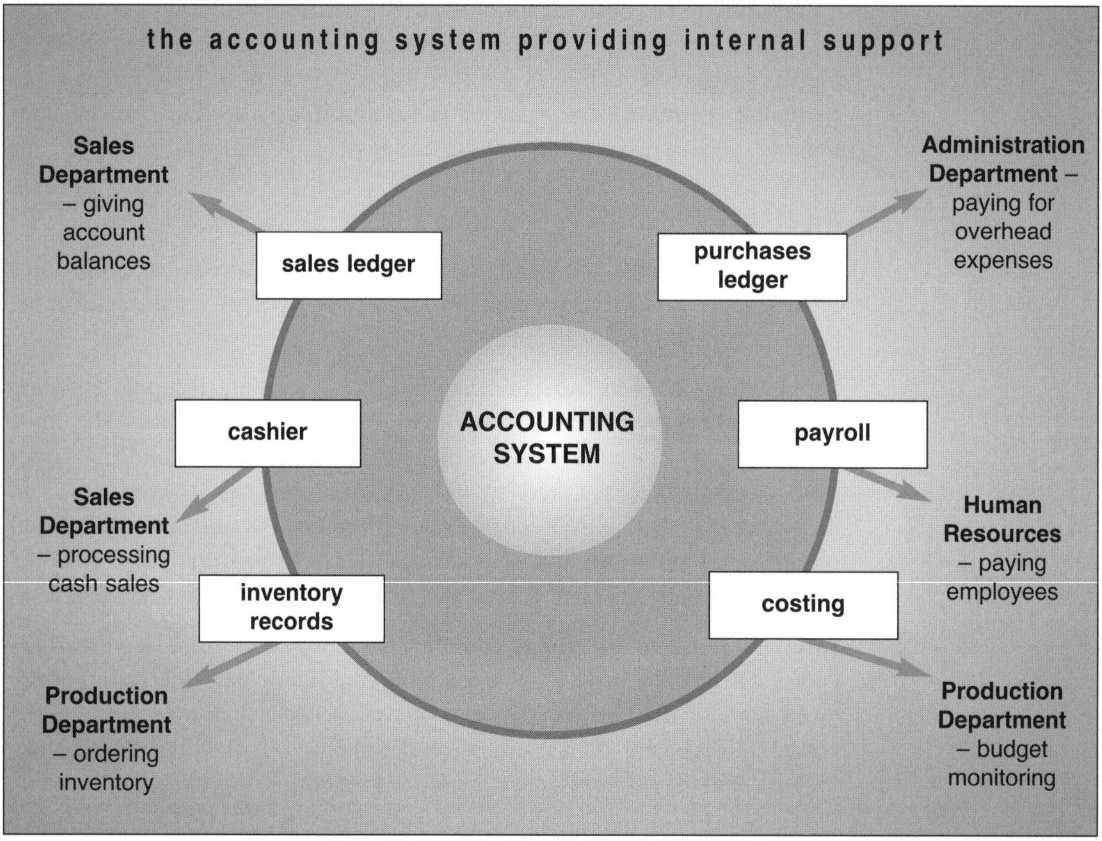

the accounting system providing internal support

Sales Department – giving account balances

sales ledger

purchases ledger

Administration Department – paying for overhead expenses

cashier

ACCOUNTING SYSTEM

payroll

Sales Department – processing cash sales

Human Resources – paying employees

inventory records

costing

Production Department – ordering inventory

Production Department – budget monitoring

REPORTING LINES

the structure of the business

The diagram on the next page is based on the accounting roles in a large company and illustrates the structure of the business. The boxes with the dark grey background all represent accounting roles. You will see that the structure is set out in a series of layers of authority and responsibility. This type of structure is known as a 'hierarchy': the lowest level is made up of the book-keepers and accounts assistants, and as you move up the structure, the people involved gain both power and responsibility.

reporting lines between levels

You will also see that the arrows represent 'up and down' **reporting lines** within the organisation. A reporting line simply means that the people lower down in the structure always report to the next layer up: accounts assistants

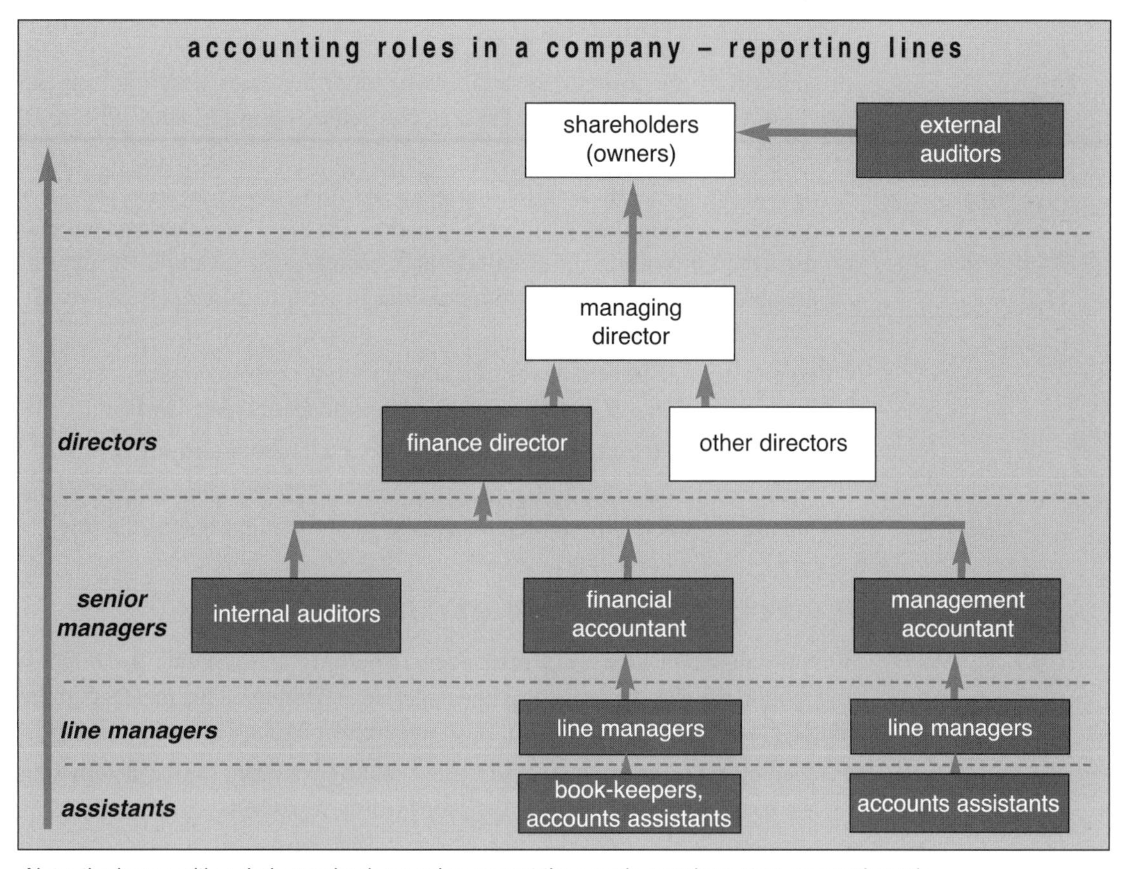

Note: the boxes with a dark grey background represent the people carrying out an accounting role.

report to line managers, who in turn report to the senior managers, who in turn report to the directors of the company.

The word 'report' here has various meanings. For example, a lower level is able to pass on to a higher level:

- specific information that is required or has been requested
- regular reports that are needed
- day-to-day work for approval and authorisation
- complaints about the work, work conditions or colleagues
- suggestions about how to improve the way the work is organised

It follows that the higher level in the company has the authority to:

- request information
- commission reports
- approve and authorise work carried out at the lower level
- deal with complaints and resolve the issue (or pass it to the next level up)
- organise discussions about the way the work is organised

other reporting lines

In addition to the formal 'up and down' reporting lines described on the previous two pages there are other identifiable reporting lines within an organisation. These include:

- people **on the same level** of authority (traditionally known as 'peers') – possibly working in a different section of the same department and regularly providing information and reports, for example a payroll assistant providing details to the cashier of cash required for the weekly cash wage packets
- people **on a different level** of authority and reported to for a specific function within the organisation, for example an accounts assistant
  - reporting to a training manager to have a talk about training needs
  - reporting as a representative of the accounts department elected to the company social committee to arrange the next night out on the town

the need for effective working

If an organisation is to work effectively, smoothly and without any hitches, it is important that the reporting lines operate efficiently. This means that the management of the organisation must ensure, for example, that:

- accounting tasks must be carefully checked by a more senior person – eg the issue of a sales invoice, the preparation of payroll
- accounting tasks must be authorised – eg the approval for payment of a purchase invoice, processing of payroll
- problems with any accounting system should be reported to a higher authority
- requests for information or a report should be clear and a realistic timescale indicated

The same holds true for reporting lines which involve people on the same level or people such as training managers.

It is critical that all employees should know

- the identity and status of the people to whom they should report
- what they have to report

If this is not made clear to employees there will be communication problems with the reporting lines, errors are likely to be made and complaints will be received. This could result in money losses and damage to the reputation of the organisation. As mentioned earlier, in a small business the accounting tasks are likely to be carried out by a limited number of people. In this case there will not be many reporting lines but the need for efficiency by the few people involved will become all the more important.

Chapter Summary

- **Finance** involves providing and managing funds and resources for an organisation such as a business, whereas **accounting** is a system for recording, analysing and reporting financial transactions and the financial position of a business.

- **Accounting** has a number of basic roles within a business, including the recording of financial information, financial reporting, forecasting, planning and managing.

- **Financial accounting** deals with the reporting of past financial transactions and their presentation in financial statements both for internal and external use.

- **Management accounting** provides past and projected financial data to managers so that forward planning can take place in the form of budgets, and decisions made about the use of resources.

- **Book-keepers** and **accounts assistants** deal with the basic financial records of an organisation in a number of defined areas:
  - sales order processing
  - purchasing
  - cashiering
  - payroll
  - costing
  - inventory control

- **Accountants** are the qualified managers of the accounting function. They may be line managers (supervisors) or more senior managers and are likely to have a specific area of responsibility.

- **Auditors** are accountants whose role it is to check that accounting procedures have been followed correctly and that no shady practices are taking place. Internal auditors are employees of the organisation and look over its accounting systems; external auditors are independent outsiders who are contracted by the shareholders of larger companies to validate the accounts.

- The accounting functions within an organisation provide support to other departments and information about the financial implications of their activities.

- A **reporting line** is the direct relationship between a manager and the people who work under him/her. It involves the passing of information, suggestions and complaints. Well-developed reporting lines are essential in any well-run organisation, especially the larger organisations.

Key Terms

finance	providing and managing funds and other resources for an organisation
book-keeping	recording financial transactions
accounting	recording, analysing and reporting financial information
financial accounting	analysis and reporting of past financial transactions in financial statements
management accounting	providing past and projected financial information for managers to help with planning, decision making and control
stakeholder	a person or organisation that has an interest in the financial performance of a business
internal auditing	internal checking of the financial records by an employee of the organisation
external auditing	external checking of the financial records by independent accountants
reporting line	the line of communication between different levels within an organisation

Activities

1.1 Which one of the following jobs can best be described as a job in 'finance'?

(a) bank lending officer

(b) management accountant

(c) book-keeper

1.2 Which one of the following jobs can best be described as a job in 'accounting'?

(a) mortgage lender

(b) auditor

(c) book-keeper

1.3 A financial accountant is a person who

(a) prepares an income statement for the last financial year

(b) sets budgets for the next financial year

(c) checks the accounts of a business

Which one of these options is correct?

1.4 A management accountant is a person who

(a) prepares an income statement for the last financial year

(b) checks the accounts of a business

(c) sets budgets for the next financial year

Which one of these options is correct?

1.5 Explain the difference between an internal auditor and an external auditor.

1.6 The diagram below shows the organisational structure of an accounts department in a small business which buys and sells goods on credit.

Study the diagram and answer the questions that follow.

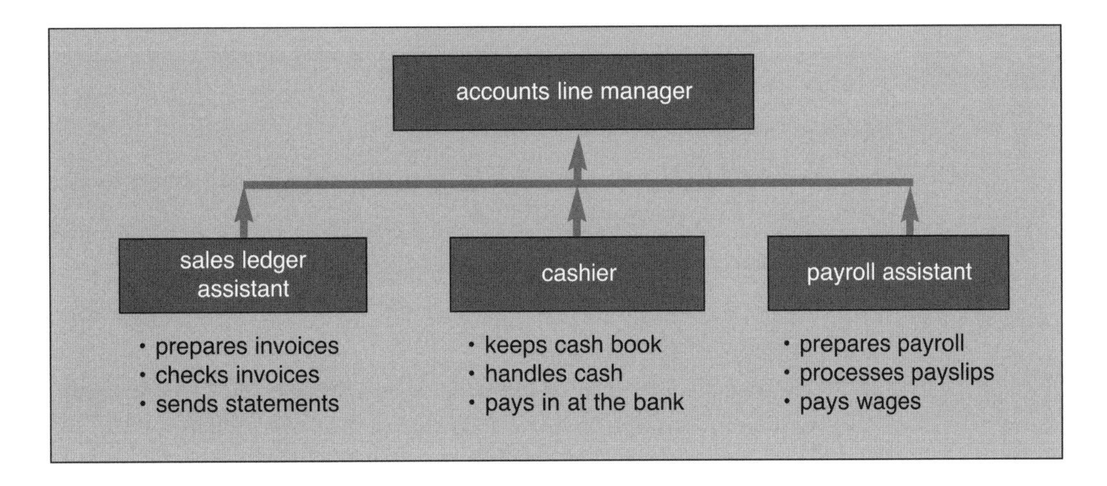

(a) Identify the three reporting lines in the diagram.

(b) Which assistant would the line manager ask if she wanted a report on customers who were bad payers?

(c) If the payroll assistant wanted to complain that there were not the right number of £20 notes available for the wage packets, to whom would he complain

(1) in the first place?

(2) in the second place, if there was still a problem?

(d) What other 'assistant level' accounting roles might also feature in this diagram, which shows a business that buys and sells goods on credit?

2 Efficiency and regulation in the workplace

this chapter covers...

This chapter examines the way in which the accounting and finance function of a business should be run so that the organisation operates smoothly and efficiently.

This means that the business should remain solvent – ie have enough money with which to pay its debts as they become due.

The business should also comply with legal requirements and internal policies and procedures. These cover areas such as:

- *accounting and finance: regulations relating to*
  - *keeping the accounts and other records*
  - *ordering goods and services*
  - *payments (cash handling, writing cheques, operating the bank account)*
  - *payroll processing*
  - *storing documents*
- *a code of conduct for the office: use of the internet, employee conduct*
- *health and safety: maintaining a safe and hazard-free working environment*
- *confidentiality: dealing with customer details, processing employee payroll*
- *'green' issues: saving energy and other resources to help increase efficiency*

Some of these procedures are based on regulations set down in law, and this will be highlighted where appropriate in the chapter, although it should be stressed that knowledge of individual laws is not required.

A SMOOTH RUNNING ORGANISATION

the need for efficiency

The last chapter explained how the accounting and finance functions of an organisation support the other departments by providing information, for example:

- customer account balances given by sales ledger staff to sales reps
- amounts of cash sales given by a cashier to the sales department

It is critical that this information is:

- **complete** – all the information needed is provided
- **accurate** – the information must be 100% correct
- **on time** – the information should be provided within the given timescale

If all these three conditions listed above are fulfilled by the staff working in accounting and finance roles, it contributes to the **efficiency** of the organisation – its smooth running and its profitability.

'Efficiency' can be described as 'achieving the right result with the minimum of wasted time, effort or expense.' Efficiency is an important objective for any organisation.

the need for solvency

'**Solvency**' means being able to pay your debts when they are due. You are 'solvent' when you can pay your debts and 'insolvent 'when you cannot.

This principle of solvency is important on a personal basis. If you cannot repay your mortgage or a credit card debt you can end up in court or with a default notice on your credit record. For a business organisation – for example a chain of shops, a bank or a football club – the inability to pay debts when they are due means that the business has become insolvent. This can result in court action, closure of the business and the loss of jobs. It also means that suppliers who are owed money are likely to lose most or all of what they are owed.

The law uses different terms to describe the situation when different types of business become involved in insolvency proceedings:

- individuals, eg sole traders, become **bankrupt**
- companies go into **administration** – this a 'half-way house' situation where an independent body (often a firm of accountants) is appointed to keep the business trading and to try and rescue the situation
- companies go into **liquidation** – the business is broken up

How does all this relate to the efficiency of the accounting and finance function of an organisation such as a business? A business needs to know that it will have enough money in the bank to be able to pay its debts. This means that the accounting and finance function will have to provide accurate and complete information to management about:

- how much money it has **at present**
- how much money it will have coming in and going out **in the future**

Specifically it will need to know accurate details of:

money in:

- the balance of money in the bank account
- the amounts coming in from customers and when they are due

money out:

- the amounts due to its suppliers and for other expenses and when they are due

All this will be computed by the business in a budget known as a **cash flow forecast**, which you will need to draw up in your later studies. The sources of information include:

- the bank account in the cash book
- data from the sales ledger showing what is due in from customers, and when
- data from the purchases and general ledgers showing what is due to suppliers and for other expenses, and when

Again, it must be stressed that the information provided by the various sections of the accounting and finance function must be accurate and complete, and provided on time.

the need for working capital

The surplus of

- money in, money due and money that can be quickly realised . . . over
- money due to be paid out

is known as **working capital**.

As long as 'money in, money due in and money realisable' is greater than 'money to be paid out', working capital is positive and the business can pay its way and is **solvent**. Careful management of working capital by the accounting and finance function is therefore very important if the business is to remain solvent. There are some basic rules to observe:

- pay money (cash, cheques) into the bank account as soon as possible; do not leave it for a long time in the the office before processing it

- negotiate good ('long') terms with your suppliers - ie pay them as late as you can without breaching any agreements, eg after 60 days
- make sure your credit customers pay up on time and try and keep the payment terms as 'short' as possible, ie 30 days rather than 90 days

So, if you pay in at the bank at least once a week, offer 30 days terms to your customers and pay your suppliers after 60 days you are making efficient use of your resources and should have enough working capital to keep you trading.

But problems can arise when there is less money coming in than going out. A new business can sometimes run into trouble, for example, if does not manage its working capital efficiently, as the following Case Study shows.

Case Study

JIMMY CASH: WORKING CAPITAL PROBLEMS

situation

Jimmy Cash has recently started business importing home alarm systems. He has put £25,000 of his savings into the bank and negotiated with four main suppliers who have asked for settlement of their invoices within 30 days.

Jimmy has been phoning around to sell his products to shops and mail order firms. He is pleased with the response, although a number of his customers have asked for payment terms of 60 days, saying that 'You will have to give me 60 days if you want the business'.

Sales for the first three months go well and Jimmy has taken on two new employees to deal with the volume of orders received. Things have been so busy in this period that Jimmy has been unable to get to the bank very often to pay in the cheques that have started to arrive. He has also received calls from two of his suppliers chasing payment of their invoices and threatening cutting off supplies if he does not pay up. He is also aware that some of his customers have not settled their first invoices. At the end of the three months he gets a call from the bank asking him to call in to discuss an unauthorised £2,000 overdraft which has appeared on his bank account.

Jimmy asks for your help and advice.

solution

You tell Jimmy that he is in a dangerous situation because he has not managed his working capital properly and may be insolvent, ie he may not be able to settle his debts (to the bank and his suppliers) from the money coming in from his sales to customers.

You advise Jimmy

- to request the bank to allow him to pay off the overdraft over the next six months
- to chase up any customers who are late paying and to bank their cheques
- to try and negotiate a longer payment period from his suppliers

Jimmy has basically ignored the need for careful cash management, and despite running a successful business, is in immediate danger of becoming insolvent.

ORGANISATIONAL POLICIES AND PROCEDURES

The remainder of this chapter deals with the **policies and procedures** set down by an organisation for dealing with a variety of areas, including the accounting function and also aspects such as health and safety at work and employment issues. These regulations are often set down in a series of manuals which should be updated regularly and readily available for reference by employees. You need to know that many of the principles set out in these manuals will be established in law, but you will not need to know about the laws themselves.

We will first describe the **policies and procedures** which affect the accounting and payroll functions of an organisation.

REGULATIONS FOR ACCOUNTING RECORDS

maintaining accounting records – companies

The law relating to limited companies (Companies Act) requires that companies should keep the following accounting records:

- records of entries made of payments received and made by the company and a description of what each entry is
- a record of the assets (items owned) and liabilities (items owed)
- records of inventory (stock) held

These records comprise financial documents and books of account such as purchase orders, invoices, credit notes, daybooks, cash book, petty cash book and, importantly, a full set of ledger accounts.

This is a description of a fairly standard system of accounting records. An important objective of any company is that this system should be accurate, complete and up-to-date.

The reason (in law) for this is that this information should be readily available for the production of the company financial statements (income statement and statement of financial position) which provide the shareholder owners with a picture of the state of the financial health of the company.

The law also states that companies have to send to Companies House (a government agency) their annual financial statements, and make an annual return, giving details of the company ownership. If these are late or not sent at all the company directors may be substantially fined. It is therefore essential that the accounting and finance function maintains the accounting records so that these returns can be made promptly and fines avoided.

accounting records – other organisations

The principles that apply to the accounting records of companies are also applied to other business organisations.

Sole trader and partnership accounting systems, whether paper-based or on computer, should be:

- systematic
- thorough
- accurate
- up-to-date
- accessible – so that information can be extracted for the owners and managers (a need illustrated in the Case Study on page 17)

retention of accounting records

Another requirement for the smooth running of an organisation is that its accounting records should be retained in accessible form in case of future queries, or even future legal action against the organisation.

Businesses normally have a retention policy stating that records are kept for six years, plus the current year. The reasons for this are based on law. Tax and company law generally require records to be kept for at least six years.

Also, if anyone wants to take a legal action against an organisation based on a contract that has been disputed or broken, they must do so within six years of the date when the dispute arose. This is another reason why all accounting records such as ledgers and financial documents are kept for at least six years – they may be needed as evidence in court. Fortunately this rarely happens.

REGULATIONS FOR PAYROLL RECORDS

maintaining payroll records

Payroll records are very sensitive because they involve the rates of pay of all the employees of an organisation. They have to be maintained:

- accurately – because they involve personal pay
- securely – to avoid fraud taking place
- confidentially – because of their sensitive nature

More often than not payroll records are kept on computer. Organisations should regulate access to this electronic data very strictly, normally through the use of passwords issued only to authorised personnel.

The body that regulates payroll (and also VAT) is the government agency HM Revenue & Customs, which is normally abbreviated to 'HMRC'. From time to time HMRC inspectors can visit a business and ask to inspect the payroll records with the intention of detecting any tax frauds or innocent mistakes. It is therefore essential that all payroll records – whether paper-based or computerised – are complete, accurate and up-to-date at all times. These records include:

- wages sheets and deductions working sheets
- calculations of wages
- details of income tax and National Insurance deducted
- tax forms such as P45s and the annual payroll return made to HMRC
- details of benefits paid to employees such as fuel allowance and other expenses

These inspections are very rigorous and businesses have to provide full details of all transactions and copies of company credit card statements in the case of expenses. If HMRC detects any fraud or major errors it can demand repayment of lost tax and impose fines. If the annual payroll return to HMRC in May is not sent or is seriously delayed, a fine may have to be made.

The message to staff working in payroll must therefore be that the payroll records must always be accurate, complete and up-to-date and kept securely and confidentially.

retention of payroll records

HMRC require that payroll records are kept for a period of three years following the tax year to which they relate. In other words, employers must keep the current year's records, plus those for the previous three years. It is quite common, however, for organisations to keep six years' worth of payroll records, simply because this procedure then ties in with the 'six years plus current year' ruling for normal accounting records.

REGULATIONS FOR VAT RECORDS

maintaining VAT records

HM Revenue & Customs also regulates the UK indirect tax **Value Added Tax** (VAT) which is charged on sales of goods and services and paid regularly by the organisation to the government.

Avoidance of charging VAT – which of course means that the customer has to pay less – is a very serious offence as it is depriving the government of important income. HMRC regularly sends inspectors to organisations to ensure that their VAT records are in order. If they find that VAT has not been charged or paid over to the government, either through fraud or by mistake, they can demand back payment of the VAT that should have been charged and can issue fines. There are reported cases of businesses that have become insolvent because they have not been able to afford the back payments demanded by HMRC!

It is therefore very important that the accounting records and financial documents which involve VAT are complete and in order. Any calculations using the VAT rate must use the correct percentage for the appropriate date, as the government has a habit of changing the VAT rate from time to time, as part of its economic policy of controlling spending.

The accounting records and financial documents involved include:

- invoices and credit notes
- receipts and petty cash vouchers
- sales and purchases day books
- sales returns and purchases returns day books
- the cash book and the petty cash book
- the VAT account in the double-entry book-keeping system

As noted above, it is critical that these records and documents are accurately completed and checked by the accounting staff as a matter of daily routine.

the VAT return - dealing with errors

VAT due to the government is calculated by an organisation by completing an online **VAT Return** on the HMRC website.

Overall responsibility for the completion of the online form is normally given to a line manager or accountant, but the figures that are entered on it are likely to be drawn up and entered by accounting staff at assistant level. The accounting information includes totals such as:

- sales made for the period by the organisation
- the VAT charged by the organisation on the sales
- purchases and expenses paid by the organisation for the period
- the VAT paid by the organisation on the purchases and expenses

These totals should be accurate and checked; they may be taken from a computer printout or worked out manually. Inevitably mistakes will occur: a big sales invoice may be missed off, an error may be made in a manual calculation. Fortunately HMRC allow mistakes up to a limit to be adjusted in later VAT Returns. Mistakes on VAT Returns, however cost money in terms of time spent putting them right. Large errors can attract fines and fines are also payable if the VAT Return is completed very late, or not at all.

As with accounting records in general, VAT records should be retained for six years plus the current year.

AUTHORISATION PROCEDURES

reporting lines and authorisation

As mentioned in the last chapter, **reporting lines** are an important element in an accounting system. Each employee is placed within a certain level of authority and will report to a higher level which will be given the responsibility of **authorising** whatever it is that the more junior employee is required to do. Typical transactions and documents which require authorisation include:

- authorisation of purchases (the signing of purchase orders)
- the making of payments (signing cheques, BACS payment orders)
- paying in at the bank (signing the paying in slip)
- petty cash payments (signing the petty cash voucher)
- payroll processing (checking and signing the payment instructions)

If the organisation is a large one the authorisation process may be more complex. For example:

- authorising payments (including the signing of cheques) up to £1,000 may require one signature, whereas payments of £1,000 or more may require two signatures
- authorisation of payroll payments may require a senior manager's signature
- a VAT Return may require a senior manager's or director's authorisation

If, however, it is a small business organisation with only five employees, there will be far fewer regulations of this type. It may be that the 'boss' will authorise everything and will delegate this when he or she goes on holiday.

The important point of all this is that employees should

- know what needs authorising and by whom
- keep to the regulations with no short-cuts being taken

The organisation will then run far more efficiently and smoothly. If there are any problems or errors, the person responsible can be identified and the problem resolved and the errors corrected.

Some sample clauses from a 'Policies and Procedures' document for the accounting and finance function are shown on the next page. Read them through and relate them to what you have already learnt.

POLICIES AND PROCEDURES STATEMENT– ACCOUNTING AND FINANCE (extracts)

Books of account and records
Proper accounting records will be kept. The accounts systems is based around computer facilities, using Sage and Excel, but manual/paper records will also be used if appropriate. The following records will be kept:

- Appropriate control accounts (bank control, petty cash control, VAT control, salary control)
- Monthly trial balances
- Petty cash and bank accounts will be reconciled at least monthly
- VAT returns produced on the required quarterly cycle

Ordering supplies and services
Budget holders can place orders for goods or services within their budget areas, subject only to cash-flow restraints. All orders of £1,000 or more must be authorised by the budget holder, except for specific areas of expenditure where written procedures have been agreed. Under £1,000, the budget holder may delegate all ordering as appropriate. Budget holders will discuss with the Financial Controller appropriate parameters, plus maximum allowed deviations before the budget holder or senior manager is brought in, which will be documented.

Payment authorisation and Purchases Ledger
All invoices must be authorised for payment by the budget holder, although the actual checking of details may be delegated. The authorising department is responsible for checking invoices for accuracy in terms of figures and conformity with the order placed, that the services or goods have been received, and following up any problems. Finance must be informed if there are queries delaying authorisation or if payment is to be withheld for any reason.

A Purchases Ledger is operated by Finance. All incoming invoices are to be passed to Finance section as soon as they arrive. Invoices will be recorded in the Purchases Ledger within two days, unless there are coding problems. They are then passed on to budget holders for authorisation. Once authorised as above, suppliers will be paid within the appropriate timescale.

Cheque writing and signing
Signatories will only be drawn from senior staff and directors, and any new signatory must be approved by the directors before the bank is notified. All cheques for £1,000 or over require two signatories. Cheque signatories should check that the expenditure has been authorised by the appropriate person before signing the cheque. Salary payments require the signature of the Accounts Manager or Financial Controller, plus one other. Cheques should be filled in completely (with payee, amount in words and figures, and date) before cheques are signed.

Handling of cash
Petty cash will be topped up on the 'imprest' system, where the amount spent is reimbursed. It is intended for small items, up to £20. Anything over this should be paid by cheque where possible. The imprest has a balance limit of £250. The petty cash balance will be reconciled when re-storing the imprest balance, or monthly if this is more frequent. All cash collected from Finance will be signed for, and receipts will be issued for all cash returned.

OFFICE MANAGEMENT POLICIES AND PROCEDURES

An efficient organisation will have well-established and documented policies and procedures covering a wide range of issues relating to staff behaviour and office organisation. They are documented because they should be set out in in-house manuals which should be read by all staff. These include:

- a **code of conduct**: covering issues such as the use of the internet and emails, mobile phones, drug and alcohol policy,
- **health and safety**: maintaining a safe and hazard-free working environment
- **confidentiality**: ensuring security of customer data
- **'green' policies**: saving the planet through conservation of energy and recycling

We will deal with each of these in turn in the next few pages.

People issues such as dealing with equal opportunities, harassment, grievances and discipline are dealt with in Chapter 4.

a code of conduct

A code of conduct will define acceptable and unacceptable staff behaviour. An efficient office will not tolerate behaviour which will disrupt the normal work flow, as in the following two cases:

> No employee is to start work, or return to work while under the influence of alcohol or drugs. A breach of this policy is grounds for disciplinary action, up to and including termination of employment.
>
> Using the organisation's computer resources to seek out, access or send any material of an offensive, obscene or defamatory nature is prohibited and may result in disciplinary action.

Harsh rules, however, do not always increase efficiency. Some employers allow the use of the internet or mobile phones in employees' free time at work and find that this enhances employees' work rate and efficiency.

It is assumed, anyway, that all accounting staff are models of good behaviour!

HEALTH AND SAFETY AT WORK

Responsibility for health and safety in the workplace lies both with the **employee** and the **employer**. You should be aware that there are many different laws governing this area, the most well-known of which is the **Health and Safety at Work Act**. You do not need to know these laws but you should be aware of the principles which they establish. Their aims are:

- to ensure that health and safety measures are introduced and observed both by employers and employees
- to specify the rights and responsibilities of employers and employees
- to enable employees to obtain compensation in the case of injury or ill health caused by conditions in the workplace

We will first describe the employer's responsibilities.

Health and Safety Policy Statement

The law requires that every employer who employs five or more employees must draw up a written **Health and Safety Policy Statement**. This document often takes the form of a loose-leaf manual which can be updated from time to time. The Statement must be shown to every employee. Employers then obtain each employee's signature on a form saying that they have read it.

The document (see illustration below) includes all the details of:

- the names of the people responsible for health and safety
- the need for safety when employees operate machinery or handle unsafe substances (eg bleach!) or lift heavy objects (see picture below)
- the need and procedures for employees to report accidents, serious illnesses or fatalities in the workplace
- the forms needed (including copies) for reporting accidents and hazards

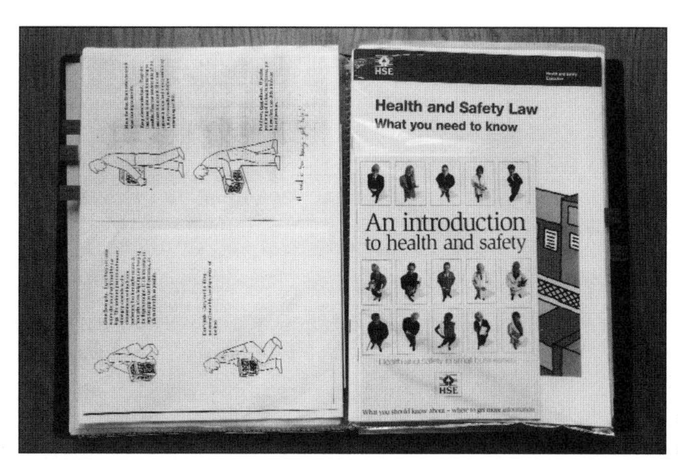

a health and safety statement

the Health and Safety 'poster'

Employers are also required to display a poster produced by the Health and Safety Executive, or provide an approved leaflet which usefully summarise the employer's obligations. An extract from the poster is shown below.

the accident book

Employees should also be made familiar with the 'accident book'. This is a record of accidents which occur in the workplace and should be completed each time there is some form of mishap. Employers should have a trained 'first aider' on the staff who will be able to treat accidents and injuries.

display screens

There are detailed regulations set down for the use by employees of

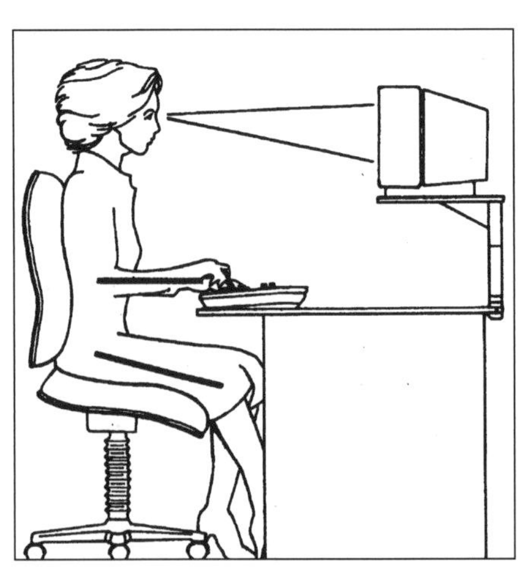

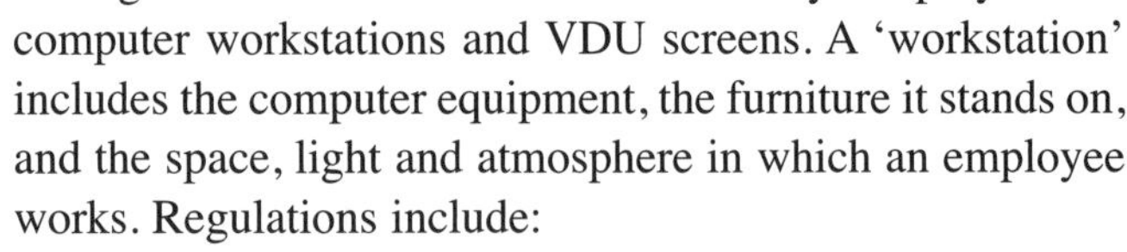

computer workstations and VDU screens. A 'workstation' includes the computer equipment, the furniture it stands on, and the space, light and atmosphere in which an employee works. Regulations include:

- employees must have regular breaks
- employees must be offered eye tests
- equipment and furniture must conform to strict standards of safety and comfort

The efficiency of an office will depend to a great degree on the level of comfort offered by the physical environment. A long time without any breaks spent inputting batches of invoices, for example, could cause errors and omissions.

emergency procedures

Employees should be made familiar with the emergency procedures for evacuating the building in the event of fires and bomb threats. They should know how to sound the alarm.

employee responsibilities for health and safety

An efficient workplace also means that employees have to take care over the way they organise not only their personal space, but also the way in which they treat the whole of the office. Any hazards should be dealt with or reported by the employee, depending on what it is. Hazards that can be avoided by employees include:

- electrical problems – trailing leads and cables
- blockages and obstacles to progress – filing drawers left open, waste bins in the way, boxes stacked up in corridors
- fire doors wedged open (ie safety doors that normally swing shut)
- employees taking unnecessary risks – standing on chairs and desks, lifting items that are too heavy or not bending properly when lifting
- employees getting too excited – running around the office, playing practical jokes, tripping people up
- using harmful substances without wearing protective clothing – for example pouring bleach down a blocked toilet and not wearing gloves
- using a computer workstation and not taking regular breaks or not using suitable seating (see previous page)

In short, health and safety involves a partnership between employer and employee; each has rights and responsibilities. If both are respected the result will be an efficient working environment.

ORGANISING THE WORK AREA

what is the 'work area'?

An employee's work area is not just the desk or workstation, it is the area which surrounds it, involving desk, chair and any furniture and filing cabinets in the vicinity.

The state of the work area is the responsibility of the employee – the user. The way in which it is (or is not) organised says a great deal about the user. A tidy desk normally means a tidy mind, just as an untidy work area often indicates a person who finds organisation rather a struggle.

it helps to be organised

An organised work area has a number of characteristics:

- it is tidy
- it is clean
- the user knows where everything is and can find it quickly
- everything is within easy reach
- the computer is correctly set up
- the chair is correctly adjusted for the user

The test of a well-organised work area is whether the user's colleagues can also find what they want. Suppose the user is an accounts assistant who deals with sales orders. She is out at lunch and an important customer telephones and asks if a recently issued sales order can be checked as an incorrect catalogue code may have been quoted on the document. Can the sales order be found? Is it in an organised filing system or pending tray, or is it buried under a pile of unsorted papers? Worse still, is it there at all?

In short, if a work area is organised properly, it will be:

- **effective** because tasks can be completed and the job done
- **efficient** because time (and therefore money) will not be wasted

the importance of efficiency

Examples of **efficiency** in the working environment are:

- having resources that you need within easy reach and not in a filing cabinet at the other end of the office
- carrying out tasks in the time allotted – other people may be waiting for you to finish checking documents so that they can carry out a task
- not wasting resources such as photocopy paper
- taking care of resources so that they will last, eg storing computer disks correctly

Efficiency is important not only because cutting down on wastage means greater profit for the organisation, but also because it has a direct influence on the **effectiveness** of other members of a workplace team.

employee responsibilities for the work area

Employees like to personalise their working environment in order to establish their identity in the workplace and to create a sense of security. Examples of this include photographs, small posters saying things like 'you

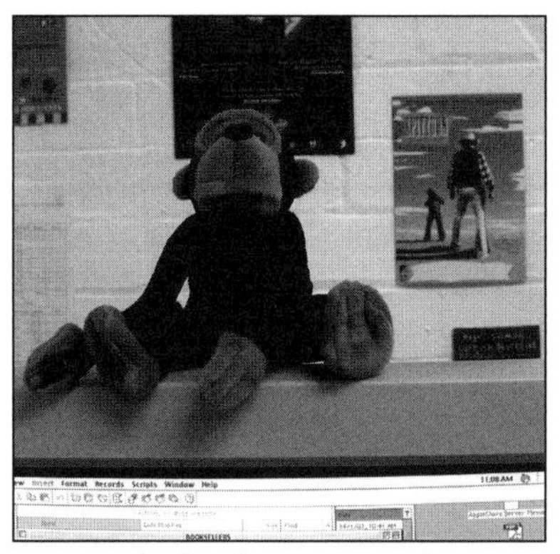
feel at home at work

don't have to be mad to work here, but it helps,' executive puzzles, fluffy toys, plants and bowls of fruit. Some modern offices operate 'hot desking' where no employee has a personal desk but has to take whatever space is available. This is not always so popular as all this homely personalisation is lost.

The organisation will, however, have **guidelines** which will regulate the extent to which an employee can put up posters, postcards and other items. It is unlikely that these guidelines will be written down, but they will normally be based on a test of what is 'reasonable' and be enforced either by a line manager or by the comments of colleagues objecting to what they think is unreasonable!

REGULATIONS FOR CONFIDENTIALITY

Employees always have to take care with confidentiality of information held both in paper records and also on computers (where security is made easier through the use of passwords). For example, payroll information should always be kept strictly confidential and not revealed to other employees.

Also, information about customers and suppliers should never be revealed to outsiders. The only exception to this is in the case of banks who suspect customers of money laundering from drug dealing or funding terrorist activities. Here the law requires that the business **must** reveal information to the police authorities.

As we have already seen, data should be retained **securely** by organisations for six years plus the current year.

the legal position

The **Data Protection Act** is an important and well-known law which protects the confidentiality of information about individuals. It applies to:

- a filing system of records held on **computer** – eg a computer database of customer names, addresses, telephone numbers, sales details
- a **manual** set of accessible records – eg a card index file system of customer details

You do not need to be able to quote the Act, but you should know that it states that personal data must be accurate, kept only as long as necessary and kept securely. It requires that an organisation should not reveal, without permission, information about its customers to other customers or any information about its employees.

'GREEN POLICIES' IN THE WORKPLACE

As momentum builds for saving the planet by conserving energy and other resources through recycling, many organisations have drawn up advisory policies and procedures for the employees. These obviously increase the efficiency of an organisation because they save energy costs; they also provide a 'feel good' factor for their employees who are environmentally aware. A typical example is shown below.

POLICIES AND PROCEDURES FOR A 'GREEN' OFFICE

Instructions to employees

Energy Conservation

1. Turn off lights when not in use and use natural light when possible.
2. Turn off, not just log off, all computers, terminals, and other office equipment at the end of every work day.
3. Activate the power down features on your computer and monitor to enter into a low-power or sleep mode when not in use.
4. Unplug equipment that drains energy even when not in use (eg fans, faxes, printers)
5. Use low energy light bulbs whenever possible.
6. Use the stairs rather than the lifts when possible.
7. Utilise videoconferencing and conference calls as an alternative to travel when possible.
8. Limit the use of space heaters.

Reduction of Materials Consumption

1. Avoid using paper by distributing and storing documents electronically.
2. Print and photocopy only what you need and double side your jobs when possible.
3. Tell staff and colleagues that you prefer double-sided documents.
4. Use the back side of old documents for faxes, scrap paper, or drafts.

Reduce Fossil Fuel Consumption and Air Pollution

1. Come to work by public transport or bike, whenever possible.
2. Share a car if you use a car.
3. Walk to work if feasible.

Minimize Waste and Increase Recycling

1. Use durable reusable drinks containers, plates, and utensils.
2. Reduce the amount of toner in documents that will be printed when possible.
3. Print documents in black and white or grayscale whenever possible.
4. Recycle paper, paper products, plastic, binders, folders, catalogues, boxes, bottles, cans, batteries, electronics, toner and ink cartridges if possible.
5. Donate old furniture and electronics through local recycling schemes.

Chapter Summary

- **Efficiency** in an organisation means achieving the right result with the minimum of wasted time, effort or expense. To achieve this the accounting and finance function must provide information, internally and to other departments. This information should be complete, accurate and on time.

- **Solvency** means paying debts when they become due. If there is a shortage of cash there is a risk of insolvency. The accounting and finance function must ensure that management are made fully aware at all times of the cash position of an organisation: cash coming in should meet the requirement for cash going out.

- Organisations should draw up formal **policies and procedures** which are documents which regulate a wide variety of areas of the business, for example accounting records and accounting procedures, health and safety in the workplace, confidentiality and conduct.

- The accounting and finance function will draw up **policies and procedures** covering its own areas of activity: accounting records, payroll records, VAT records.

- The accounting and finance function will be subject to **external regulations**, some of them set down in law, which must be complied with. Failure to do so may result in fines and extra work by accounting and finance staff.

- Policies and procedures also affect **working practices** in the accounting and finance function. These include internal requirements such as the setting of deadlines, procedures for authorisation of purchases, payments, cheques and details of who can sign different types of authorisation.

- Policies and procedures also affect the **working area** in the accounting and finance function. Strict regulation of issues such as health and safety, organisation of the workspace, secure storage of documents and confidentiality of information must be complied with if the organisation is to remain efficient.

- Guidance policies and procedures may also be drawn up by the organisation to ensure that the office becomes '**green**' – in other words environmentally friendly. This will cut down on wastage of resources such as energy and paper and so make the organisation more efficient.

Key Terms

efficiency	achieving the right result with the minimum of of wasted time, effort or expense
solvency	being able to repay your debts when they are due
working capital	the day-to-day funds that you have available to pay your debts when they are due
policies and procedures	regulations set down by an organisation for the running of defined areas of activity, eg payroll
reporting line	the line of communication between different levels and departments within an organisation
health and safety	the aspects of an organisation which involve both employer and employee having regard for a healthy and safe working environment for all concerned
confidentiality	the need for all employees not to reveal any information relating to customers and other employees to people who are not authorised to have that information
data protection	the legal requirement not to reveal without authorisation personal information held on computer or on paper records by an organisation

Activities

2.1 Which one of the following is the most accurate definition of efficiency?

(a) to complete a job as quickly as possible at all costs

(b) to complete a job with the minimum of wasted time, effort or expense

(c) to complete a job exactly as described in the Policies and Procedures

(d) to complete a job using the cheapest way of doing it

Which one of these options is correct?

2.2 Which one of the following is the most accurate definition of solvency?

(a) receiving all your customer payments on the due date

(b) having a lot of money in the bank

(c) being able to pay all your debts when they are due

(d) being able to pay all the wages on the due date

Which one of these options is correct?

2.3 If you want to improve your working capital position you should:

(a) pay your suppliers earlier

(b) get your customers to pay you earlier

(c) pay your wages earlier

(d) pay in at the bank less frequently

Which one of these options is correct?

2.4 Policies and procedures are

(a) Company rule books required for the workplace by law

(b) Rule books for business organisations drawn up by their employees

(c) HM Revenue & Customs requirements for deducting tax from employees

(d) Rules and regulations drawn up by organisations to cover different functional areas

Which one of these options is correct?

2.5 The VAT records of a business organisation should be accurate and complete so that

(a) the business becomes efficient and pays as little VAT as possible

(b) a complete and accurate VAT return may be made to HM Revenue & Customs

(c) the annual payroll return can be made to HM Revenue & Customs without any delay

(d) the credit customers of the business will pay up on time

Which one of these options is correct?

2.6 A Health and Safety Policy Statement is

(a) issued each year by the Government to help protect employees at work

(b) drawn up by employees to state their rights to personalise their working area

(c) a list of the accidents and fatalities at work each year

(d) drawn up by the employer as a guide to employees of health and safety arrangements

Which one of these options is correct?

2.7 The requirement for confidentiality means that employees of a business organisation

(a) should only reveal financial information about their own company when authorised to do so

(b) should only reveal information about their customers when they are off work premises

(c) should only reveal financial information about their own business six years after the event

(d) should never reveal to the police if they see that customers are 'laundering' money

Which one of these options is correct?

3 Working with numbers

this chapter covers...

This chapter is a practical guide showing you how to carry out the types of basic calculation that you are likely to encounter when working in accounting and finance. The important lesson here is that you should use your common sense as well as your calculator when working out a solution.

These techniques include:

- *carrying out calculations and using estimation to check what you have done*
- *using multiplication – for example, to calculate the cost of goods on an invoice*
- *dealing with percentages to calculate a variety of figures, for example:*
  - *working out and checking discounts on invoices*
  - *calculating and checking Value Added Tax on invoices*
  - *working out the levels of difference between actual and budgeted figures*
- *dealing with averages, for example calculating the average value of inventory held by a business*
- *using tables to present numbers*
- *drawing up a variety of graphs and charts which can be used in reports to illustrate numbers and trends*

BASIC CALCULATIONS

processing of numerical data

Working in finance and accounting often involves processing large volumes of figures. This may be carried out using electronic aids:

- a computer accounting program for calculating invoice totals
- a spreadsheet for processing a budget
- a calculator – maybe with a tally roll – for adding up long lists of figures, eg the total of customer cheques to be paid into the bank

accurate checking of data – estimation

In all these cases accuracy of **input** of the figures is very important and should be routinely **checked** as part of the office procedures. In the case of the addition of columns of figures, one way of checking accuracy is to carry out the procedure twice, and get somebody else to call out the figures if there is a discrepancy.

Estimation is also very important when you carry out or check a calculation. Does the total seem about right? Common sense is critical. For example, does the admin office really need to order 2,500 pens, or should it be 25?

The situation below is based on a real incident and shows the serious danger of not using common sense or checking figures properly.

Online Electronics store apologises for 49p TV error

Thousands of internet shoppers who bought a TV normally priced at £499 but quoted at an online price of 49p have been told the deal was too good to be true.

The internet store is refusing to honour the website deals and has apologised, saying the mistake in pricing was down to a "genuine internal error".

About 10,000 customers had bought the 32" TV over a Bank Holiday.

But the company has now cancelled all the orders and is giving refunds.

A company spokesperson commented that this problem was down to an unfortunate mistake "while keying in data".

using multiplication

Multiplication is commonly used when drawing up invoices and credit notes manually, and also when checking them. For example, if you receive an order for 10 red box files which cost £4.00 each, you will produce an invoice which will show: **product quantity x unit price,** ie

10 x £4.00 = £40.00

This will appear as shown in this invoice extract:

product code	description	quantity	price £	unit	total £	discount %	net £
BF-R	Box file (red)	10	4.00	each	40.00		

This is straightforward enough; you just need to make the calculation and check it and apply the estimation test. Does £40 seem a reasonable answer?

The last two columns of the above invoice, which include a percentage discount column, are left blank for now. We will explain how to calculate discounts later in this chapter. The use of percentage calculations in business is very common and is explained in the next section.

DEALING WITH PERCENTAGES

definition – a percentage is a part of a whole

The phrase 'per cent' means 'out of every hundred'.

So 50% means '50 out of every hundred.' A percentage therefore tells you what proportion one number is in relation to another. In other words, a percentage is a part of a whole, where the whole is 100. It is the top number of a fraction when the bottom number is 100:

$$50\% = \text{the fraction } \frac{50}{100} = \frac{1}{2} \quad \text{ie, a half}$$

If you go to a party where there are twenty people, your partner might use a fraction and say *'I don't know half the people here'*. This could literally be taken to mean that 10 of the 20 people, or 50% of the people are complete strangers. This example you could work out in your head, but at work the figures are not always so convenient and you will need to use a formula.

The way to work out the percentage of people your partner knows is to divide the number known (the 'part') by the total (the 'whole') and then multiply the result of this by 100. The formula is therefore:

$$\frac{\textbf{the part x 100}}{\textbf{the whole}} = \textbf{percentage of the part}$$

Suppose your partner knew 12 of the 20 people at the party. The percentage of people known would be:

$$\frac{\text{12 people x 100}}{\text{20 people}} = \text{60\% are known}$$

If only two people were known, the calculation would be:

$$\frac{2 \text{ x } 100}{20} = \text{10\% are known}$$

Then you would probably not stay at the party for very long.

working out a percentage of a given number

This is a very common use of percentages in organisations. Here you **start** with the percentage rate and use it as a number of 'hundreths' to work out the figure you need as a fraction of a given amount. It is used, for example, to calculate:

- **discounts** – an amount to subtract from a money amount
- **tax** – an amount, VAT for example, to add to sales

This is done by using the formula

$$\frac{\textbf{given percentage x amount}}{\textbf{100}} = \textbf{percentage amount}$$

Suppose you want to calculate 8% of £250. Using the formula, the calculation is:

$$\frac{\text{8 (percentage) x £250 (amount)}}{100} = \text{£20}$$

An easy way of doing this is to shift the decimal place of the percentage figure two places to the left in your head and then put this figure in a calculator and multiply it by the money amount. So in this case 8% becomes 0.08 and the calculation is simply:

0.08 x £250 = £20

Using the same principle, 12% and 50% of £250 become:

0.12 x £250 = £30

0.50 x £250 = £125

calculating discount amounts

We will now use the formula explained on the previous page to calculate a discount amount. The invoice extract shown on page 36 shows the discount given on the sales transaction. This is most likely to be **trade discount** – ie the discount given to customers who expect a discount as part of the trading relationship. In some circumstances a **bulk discount** can be given – this is where the quantity ordered or the order value is large.

Calculating discounts involves working out a percentage of the total of the products sold and then **deducting** this from the total.

The formula needed to calculate the percentage discount which will be deducted is therefore:

$$\frac{\textbf{sales total (£) x discount percentage}}{\textbf{100}} = \textbf{discount (£)}$$

Continuing the example on page 36 the sales total is £40 and the trade discount is 20%. Applying the formula, the calculation is:

$$\frac{\text{sales total (£40) x discount percentage (20)}}{100} = \text{discount of £8}$$

Note that the discount amount of £8 is not actually shown on the invoice; all you see is the amount before the discount is deducted (£40) and the net amount after the discount is deducted (£32). This may seem confusing, but it is common practice!

product code	description	quantity	price £	unit	total £	discount %	net £
BF-R	Box file (red)	10	4.00	each	40.00	20	32.00

a note on rounding

Sometimes the discount amount will not come out as a precise '£ and pence' figure, ie to two decimal places.

The number of **decimal places** means the quantity of numbers to the right of the decimal point. In money amounts this will obviously always be 2. The calculation may produce something awkward like £91.9324 or £45.5786. In this case the four figures to the right of the decimal point will have to be **rounded up or down** to produce the correct number of decimal places to correspond with the two digits showing pence - ie 2 decimal places. In this case:

£91.93<u>24</u> becomes £91.9<u>3</u> (rounded **down** to the nearest penny)

£45.57<u>86</u> becomes £45.58 (rounded **up** to the nearest penny)

The '**rounding**' rule is therefore:

- start with the right-hand digit of the number
- if it is 5 or higher delete it and add 1 to the digit on its left
- if it is less than 5 delete it and leave the digit on the left as it is
- carry on until you have the right number of decimal places (this is normally 2 decimal places in the case of money amounts in accounting)

adding VAT (sales tax) to an invoice

The invoice used in the example on the last few pages is also likely to include Value Added Tax (VAT), which is a sales tax. This is worked out as percentage of the net total after any trade discount has been calculated. Like most taxes, VAT is quoted as a percentage rate, and like most taxes VAT varies from time to time. In this book VAT is quoted at a rate of 20%.

The invoice with the VAT calculation will appear as follows:

product code	description	quantity	price £	unit	total £	discount %	net £
BF-R	Box file (red)	10	4.00	each	40.00	20	32.00
						Total	32.00
						VAT @ 20%	6.40
						TOTAL	38.40

The VAT calculation is as follows:

VAT is calculated as a percentage of the cost of the goods. If invoiced goods, as here, cost £32, the VAT (at the standard rate of 20%) is calculated as:

$$\frac{£32 \times 20}{100} = £6.40$$

Important note: if the amount of VAT calculated comes out at more than 2 decimal places, you normally **delete all digits** to the right of the 2 decimal places. This is different from the rounding rule set out at the top of the page.

Remember that whereas the discount of £8.00 is **deducted** from the total to be charged to produce a net total of £32.00, the VAT of £6.40 is an indirect tax and should be **added on** to produce the final total of £38.40.

calculating VAT when it is included in the total

Sometimes you may have to deal with a low value invoice or receipt which quotes a figure which includes VAT at a certain rate, but does not actually tell you what the VAT amount or the cost price is. You may have to calculate this VAT amount and the cost before VAT to enter in the books; for example in the petty cash book.

Let us take an example of a receipt or invoice for £24.00 for some stationery. This includes the cost of the stationery (100%) and also the VAT (20%) added to this cost. The total amount therefore equates to 120% of the cost.

The formula to use in this case is:

$$\frac{\textbf{VAT percentage}}{\textbf{100\% + VAT percentage}} \times \textbf{total amount(£)} = \textbf{VAT content(£)}$$

Applying this formula to the total figure of £24.00, the calculation is:

$$\frac{\text{20\% (VAT\%)}}{\text{120\% (VAT\% + 100)}} \times \text{£24.00} = \text{a VAT content of £4.00}$$

Therefore the £24.00 total amount is made up of a cost price of £20.00 and VAT of £4.00 (£20.00 is £24.00 minus £4.00).

alternative method – the VAT fraction

If the VAT rate is 20%, another way of working out the VAT included in a total amount is to multiply the whole amount by what is known as the 'VAT fraction' of $^1/_6$, or more simply, divide the whole amount by 6.

The calculation is therefore £24.00 ÷ 6 = £4.00.

This fraction of $^1/_6$ is provided by HM Revenue & Customs. This particular fraction only works for a VAT rate of 20%. If the VAT rate changes, the VAT authorities (HMRC) change the fraction accordingly.

PERCENTAGES FOR MANAGEMENT ACCOUNTING

The application of percentages to your studies so far has concentrated on basic accounting and book-keeping, using an invoice as an example. Percentages are also very useful for reporting data, comparing the sales and profit results for different periods, for example, or commenting on the extent to which actual sales or profit results compare with the forecast made in a budget. These relate to management accounting (accounting information for decision making by managers).

percentages for comparison

There are many applications of percentages in management accounting. For example a shop owner might say that:

'60% of our total sales for the year were made in the two months before Christmas.'

This is much clearer than saying:

> *'£240,000 of our annual sales of £400,000 were made in the two months before Christmas.'*

To work out this percentage you need to use the formula:

$$\frac{\textbf{the part of the whole} \times 100\%}{\textbf{the whole}} = \textbf{the percentage}$$

In the example above, the calculation is

$$\frac{£240{,}000 \times 100\%}{£400{,}000} = 60\%$$

This is useful, for example, when the business wants to compare pre-Christmas sales with other years:

> *'60% of our sales this year were made in the two months before Christmas; this compares with a figure of 55% for last year.'*

This gives you a much clearer picture than if you said:

> *'£240,000 of our annual sales of £400,000 were made in the two months before Christmas; this compares with £192,500 out of a total of £350,000 made last year.'*

This will only give you a headache.

percentages and benchmarks

If you are studying basic costing you will know that a **benchmark** is a forecast figure which is set as a **target** by an organisation for sales or costs for a future period, for example the next year. When the end of that period is reached the organisation will compare

- the actual results, and
- the benchmark forecast

The difference between the two figures will then be calculated. This difference can be stated by means of an amount or a percentage of the benchmark (forecast) figure. If the amount or percentage is greater than what would be expected, it will need to be reported to management so that action can be taken if necessary.

The example shown below shows a comparison of two years' sales figures for a business which sells modern art pictures. Study the table and read the notes and conclusion that follow.

ART WORLD LIMITED – Annual Sales

	Forecast (benchmark) £	Actual £	Difference £	Percentage difference
Year 1	400,000	420,000	+ 20,000	5%
Year 2	420,000	407,400	– 12,600	3%

Workings:

- the first column of figures shows the forecast target sales figures
- the second column of figures shows the actual results for the year
- the third column shows the difference between the forecast and actual figures (a '+' means more than forecast, a '–' means less than forecast)
- the last column shows the difference shown as a **percentage of the forecast figure** (not the actual figure); the workings are as follows:

Year 1

$$\frac{\text{Difference (£20,000)}}{\text{Forecast/benchmark (£400,000)}} \times 100\% = 5\%$$

Year 2

$$\frac{\text{Difference (£12,600)}}{\text{Forecast/benchmark (£420,000)}} \times 100\% = 3\%$$

Conclusion

1 **Sales for Year 1** are higher than the benchmark by £20,000.

The percentage difference for Year 1 is 5%, which means that sales are 5% higher than forecast.

2 **Sales for Year 2** are lower than the benchmark by £12,600.

The percentage difference for Year 2 is 3%, which means that sales are 3% lower than forecast.

3 Management will take action if they think it is necessary.

USING AVERAGES

A technique which is useful when reporting on a series of performance figures, such as sales figures, is the use of **averages**. There are three commonly-used types of average: the mean, the median and the mode.

which average?

Suppose the finance manager of a kitchen installation business wanted to know for budgeting purposes the average job completion time in days, from initial enquiry through to final installation. He has just received the figures for the jobs completed last month. The figures are (in days):

20, 25, 35, 35, 35, 36, 37, 55, 60, 65, 65

What is the average job completion time? We will look in turn at the **mean**, **median** and **mode** averages.

the mean

The arithmetic mean is probably the most commonly-used and statistically-reliable form of average. It is also known as a '**weighted average**.'

The arithmetic mean is the sum of all the figures divided by the number of figures.

The sum of 20, 25, 35, 35, 35, 36, 37, 55, 60, 65, 65 = 468

The arithmetic mean = $\frac{468}{11}$ = 42.5 days

This tells the manager that, on average, a job takes approximately 43 days to complete. This will help him in the planning and budgeting process. Note:

- the result is not a whole number of days – rounding up to 43 is necessary
- the result takes into account all values – if there had been an exceptional job taking 165 days instead of 65, the result will have been a mean average of 568 ÷ 11 = 51.6 days, a possibly distorted result

the median

The median is the value of the middle figure in a series of figures.

Note that if there is no middle figure, as with an even number of values, the median is the arithmetic mean of the two figures nearest to the middle.

Here the median is 20, 25, 35, 35, 35, **36**, 37, 55, 60, 65, 65 = 36 days.

This will not be as helpful to the manager as the mean in this context; it is useful because it is not distorted by extreme values (eg 165 days) – the mean, however, is more reliable because an equal weighting is given to each value.

the mode

The mode is the value that occurs most often in a series.

In this case the most common period is 35 days (3 jobs), followed closely by 65 days (2 jobs). Note that these two time periods are very widely dispersed. This would suggest that this type of average is not as helpful in the planning process. The mode is more useful in areas such as market research in answering questions such as 'How much do people on average spend on a fast food meal?' or 'What is the most commonly-occurring size of T shirt?'

using the mean in inventory (stock) valuation

If you are studying basic costing you will know that it is important for a business organisation to be able to calculate its inventory (stock) value, ie the valuation of all the materials and items it holds. One method of inventory valuation is **AVCO** (short for **AV**erage **CO**st). It is very useful for inventory that is added to from time to time and mixed up with existing inventory.

Take, for example, a business importing and selling Chinese tennis rackets. It buys in its tennis rackets every month and stores them in the warehouse. Because the cost price of the rackets varies each month (due to currency fluctuations) and because the rackets are mixed up with rackets already held in inventory it becomes virtually impossible to value the rackets **unless an average cost is taken**, using the mean (weighted average) method.

The formula for this is:

$$\frac{\textbf{total cost of inventory held}}{\textbf{number of inventory items held}} = \textbf{average cost of an item of inventory}$$

If the total cost of the rackets held is £110,000 (different prices paid for consignments on different invoices over six months) and the number of rackets held is 5,500, the **average cost price** can be worked out as follows:

$$\frac{\textbf{£110,000}\text{ (cost of items)}}{\textbf{5,500}\text{ (number of items)}} = \textbf{£20}\text{ (average cost of item of inventory)}$$

In other words at the time that this calculation was made each racket in the warehouse had cost the business, on average, £20.

The business can then use this figure to work out its selling price and make sure that it makes a profit.

USING TABLES

Tables of figures are often used in accounting and finance for setting out data which is useful to management. Sometimes they can be incorporated into a report (see next chapter) to:

- provide information
- illustrate a proposal

Figures in a table which covers an extended period of time (eg 'this year' and 'last year') can usefully provide a comparison for sales, costs and profit. The technical term for this type of comparison of numbers over time is **time series analysis**.

Staff working in accounting and finance will need to know how to set out a table so that it is clear and accurate. The most common way of doing this is to use a computer spreadsheet or word processing program. A spreadsheet will also enable graphs and charts to be extracted; these can then be included in a report to illustrate data and trends.

constructing a table

If you are processing a set of figures at work you may have to construct a table; alternatively the table may be in 'pro-forma' form (ready made) or it may be output from a computer information system, or be completed as a computer spreadsheet.

The example shown below shows the sales and profit results for a limited company over a period of four years. Study the table and read the notes that follow.

Amico Ltd: Sales and Profit Statement Report

	Year 1 *£000s*	Year 2 *£000s*	Year 3 *£000s*	Year 4 *£000s*
Sales	500	970	1,430	1,912
Net profit	65	95	132	147

- the title clearly sets out what the data is
- each time period is shown in a vertical column
- each time period is clearly headed up (it could be a year, a month or a week)

- the units for the data are stated below the time period – here £000s are chosen to prevent the table being cluttered up with unnecessary zeros
- the types of data are set out in two rows and labelled in the left-hand column – ie 'Sales' and 'Net Profit' (which means profit after all expenses have been deducted)
- lines are added to clarify the table – it is not necessary in this case to draw a line under each row of data as the columns can easily be read across; if, however, there was a large number of columns, lines would be helpful

presenting and interpreting the data

The figures set out in the table on the previous page can be interpreted just by reading them, but a much better picture can be obtained by presenting the data in the form of a graph or chart which will provide a very visual concept of each trend and help the understanding of the report.

This process can be carried out manually or by using a computer spreadsheet or charting package. The graphs and charts which follow on the next few pages were produced by a simple spreadsheet program.

LINE GRAPH

The simplest form of visual representation of a time series is the **line graph**.

A line graph, which can be in a straight line or a curve, shows the relationship between two sets of data – 'variables'. One variable will always depend on the other. They are known as:

- the **independent variable** – the measurement that is at a fixed interval
- the **dependent variable** – the figure that will depend on the independent variable

A common independent variable is time, and a common dependent variable is money.

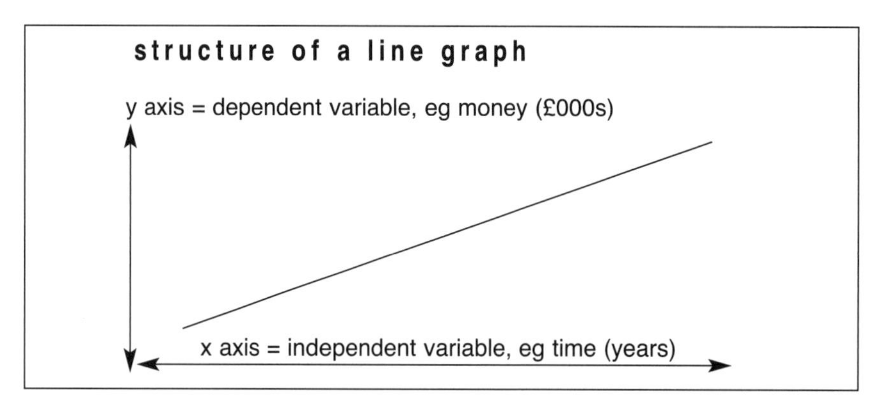

important note!

The AAT has announced that students will not be required to construct charts or diagrams in assessments. They will however be expected to encounter them as additions to reports and other communications. It is important therefore that students know how to 'read' and interpret charts such as line graphs, bar charts and pie charts. The Case Study that follows and the text on pages 48 to 51 explain how each type of chart can be useful in presenting particular types of accounting information.

Case Study

AMICO LTD: LINE GRAPH FOR SALES FIGURES

situation

You have been given the sales figures for Amico Limited for the last four years and have produced a line graph to show the trend in sales. You then need to explain to a new member of staff what you have included on the line graph.

solution

The line graph is shown below. You have added the boxes and text to show what you have explained to the new member of staff so that they will be able to 'read' and interpret the graph.

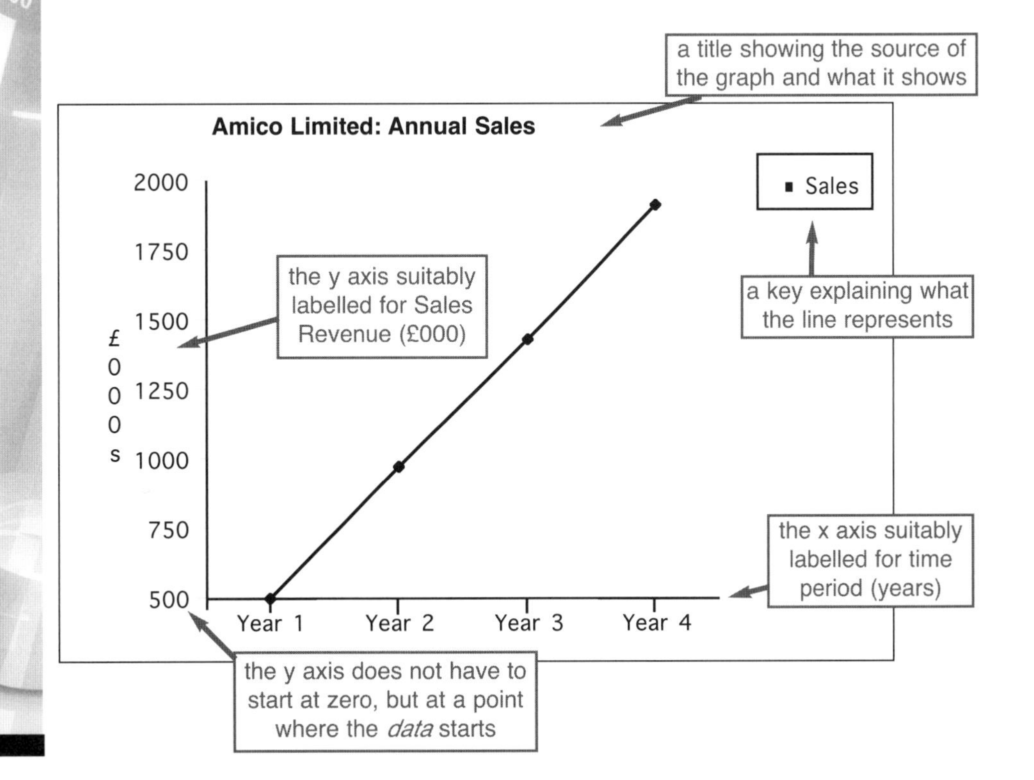

BAR CHARTS

A bar chart is a chart which sets out a series of bars, the height of which indicates the extent of the dependent variable. It is normal to set out a bar chart along the horizontal 'x' axis (so that they look like high-rise buildings) but the practice can be varied so that they stretch left to right from the 'y' axis.

Bar charts can be simple, compound or component, depending on what data comparisons need to be made.

simple bar chart

The simple bar chart is the most common type. It works on the same basis as a line graph and illustrates a trend. Set out below is a simple bar chart which uses the sales figures for Amico Limited from the table in the Case Study on the previous page. Compare it with the line graph in the Case Study.

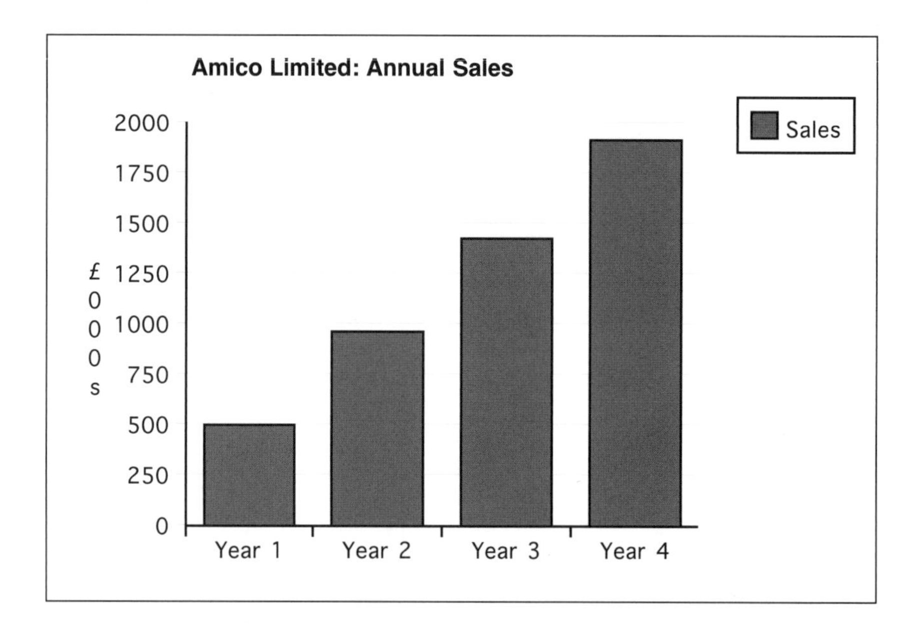

Note that:

- the labelling conventions are the same as for a line graph – here the bars are shaded in grey
- the 'y' axis goes down to zero – the whole length of the bar is needed (this is different from the line graph scaling)
- the bars are separated – this is common, but not essential – they can be drawn so that their sides touch

compound bar chart

Just as it is possible to have a line graph with more than one line, it is also possible to be given a bar chart with more than one set of data for each dependent variable – eg sales for different types of product. This is known as a **compound bar chart**.

The example below shows the sales figures for product types X, Y and Z for Amico Limited.

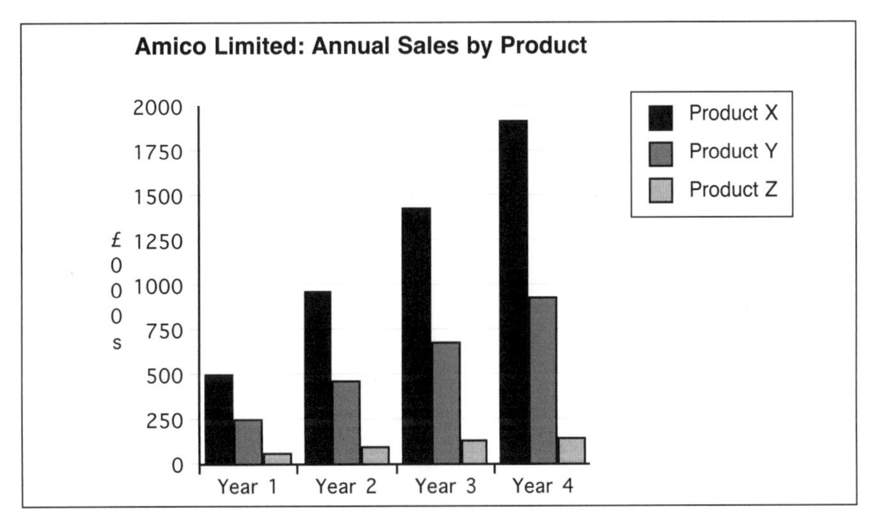

component bar chart

A component bar chart is a bar chart which divides each bar into segments, showing how the total for each bar is made up. For example, if the annual sales totals for Amico Limited were made up of totals for three sales divisions A, B and C, each bar could be shown as having three segments.

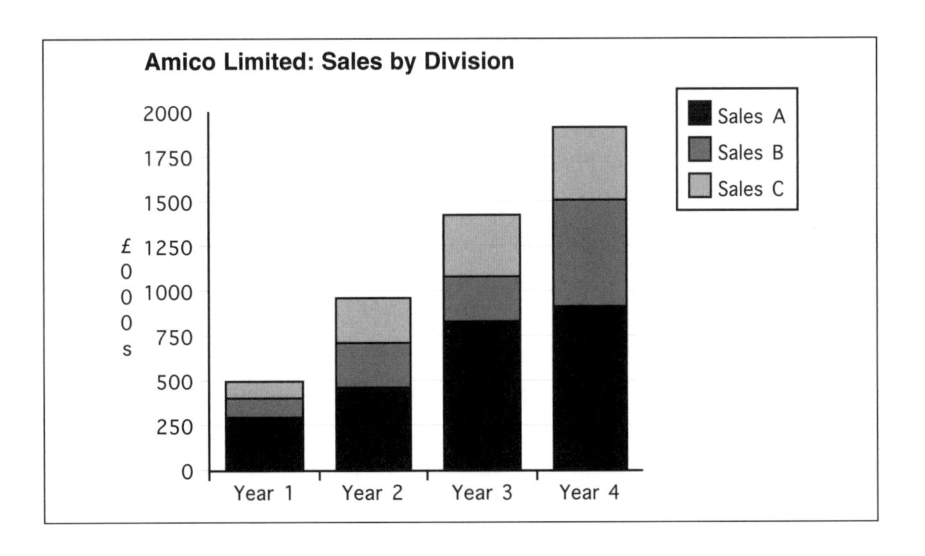

percentage component bar chart

Another way of presenting the sales data is to express the divisional sales figures as **percentages** of the annual sales total in a percentage component bar chart. Each bar is then the same height, ie 100%, and the subdivisions show the trends of divisional sales over the four years.

In the example below you can see that the performance of Division A as a percentage of total sales fluctuates substantially each year, a trend that is not shown on the ordinary component chart (previous page) which indicates a steady increase. This is the type of trend that the management might be advised to investigate.

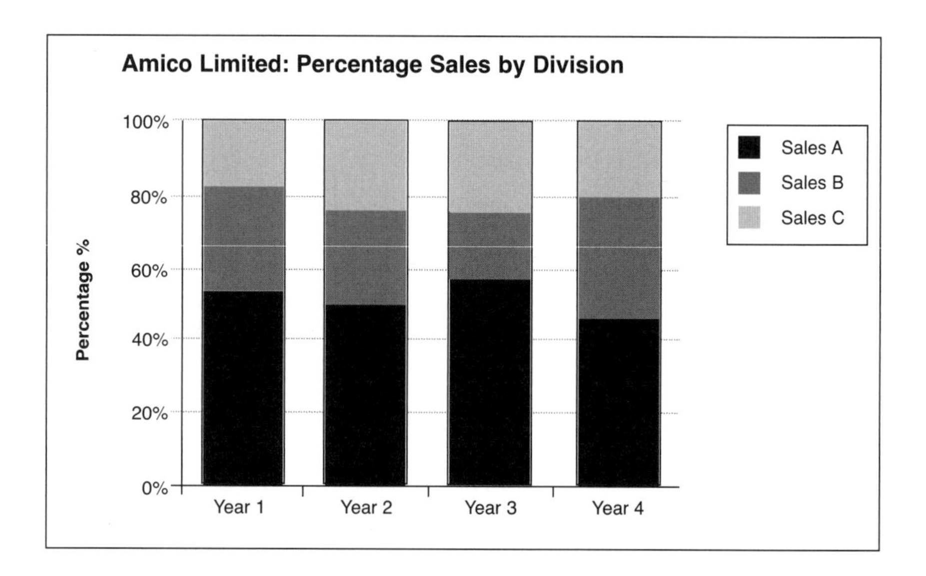

PIE CHARTS

A **pie chart** is a circle divided into sectors to represent the parts of a whole in their correct proportions. It is called a pie chart because, like a meat or fruit pie, it is cut into 'slices.'

Line graphs and bar charts are suitable for the presentation of **time series** data – data which varies from time period to time period. Pie charts, on the other hand, are useful in showing the breakdown of a whole into its constituent parts **at a particular moment in time**.

If you take Amico Limited's sales figures for Year 1 you will equate the total sales of £500,000 with the whole pie circle. This will be divided into segments, each of which will proportionally represent a divisional sales figure.

The divisional sales figures are as follows:

Division A	£300,000
Division B	£110,000
Division C	£90,000
Total sales	£500,000

The pie chart for Year 1 looks like this:

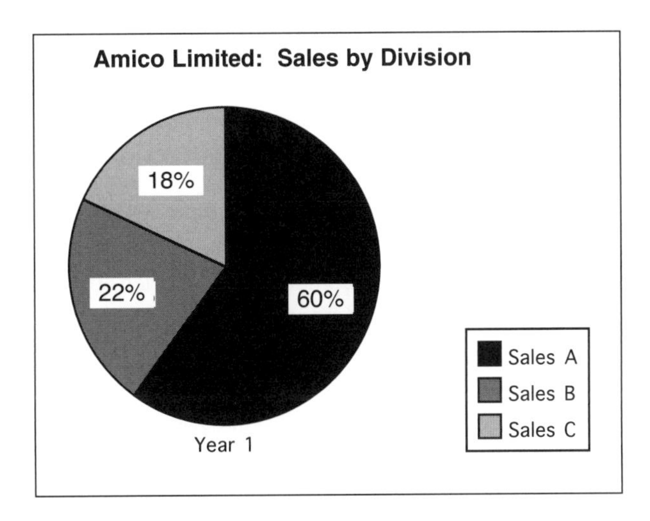

Note that the segments are labelled with the percentage sales. Remember that a percentage is worked out as:

$$\frac{\text{the part} \times 100}{\text{the whole}} = \text{percentage} \ldots \text{ in this case, } \frac{£300{,}000 \times 100}{£500{,}000} = 60\%$$

You may find that you have a report which presents comparative pie charts. For example, the sales figures for two years could be compared as follows:

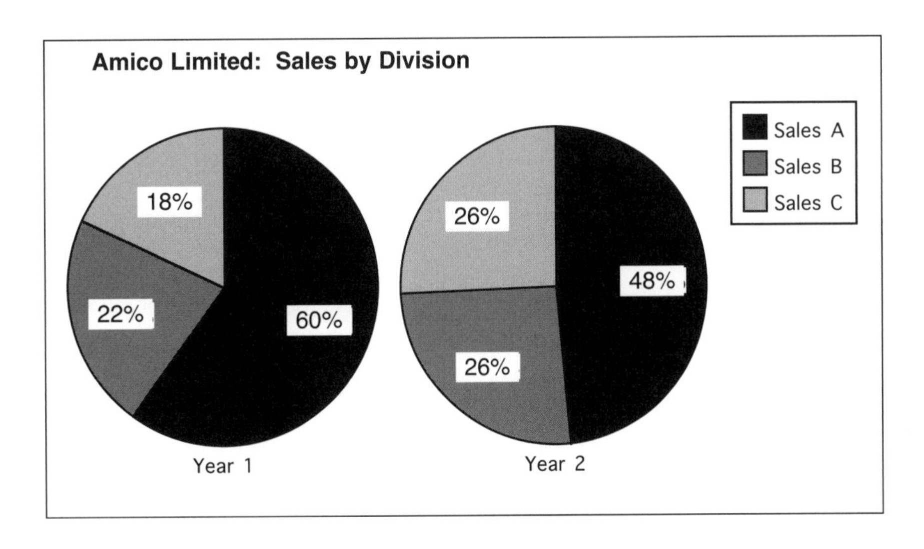

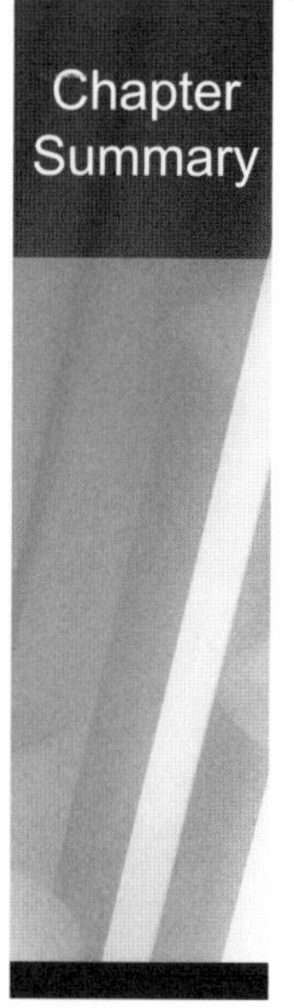

- **Calculations** – addition, subtraction, multiplication and division – carried out in the workplace should always be checked for accuracy, firstly by using common sense estimation and then ideally by another employee carrying out the same calculation.

- **Percentages** are based on the concept of fractions and are commonly used in accounting and finance, for example in the calculation of discounts, Value Added Tax, comparison of performance data, and in budgeting for measuring the difference between actual and benchmark (forecast) figures.

- **Averages** are used in accounting and finance, for example in calculating inventory (stock) values in the AVCO (average cost) process.

- The **presentation of numerical data** in table format is an important skill for working in accounting and finance. Tables are often incorporated in reports for management, sometimes supported by graphs and charts which illustrate results and trends very effectively.

Key Terms

estimation — using a common sense approach to calculation by seeing if the answer produced seems 'reasonable'

percentage — 'per cent' means 'out of every hundred,' so a percentage is the top number of a fraction where the bottom number is 100

discount — a percentage of an amount deducted from that amount

decimal place — the number of digits (numbers) to the right of the decimal point; £ and p are quoted to two decimal places, eg £4.99

rounding — in the case of £ and p, reducing the number of digits to two decimal places by rounding up or down to the nearest p

benchmark — in costing this is a forecast figure for future performance (eg sales) against which the actual figure is then compared

mean average — the sum of a series of figures divided by the number of figures – this is also known as a 'weighted average'

time series — a series of data collected regularly over a period of time, eg annual sales figures

line graph — a visual representation of a time series set out in a line

bar chart — a chart which sets out a series of bars, the height of which indicates the extent of the value that varies

pie chart — a circle divided into sectors to represent in the correct proportion the parts of a whole – like a pie divided into 'slices'

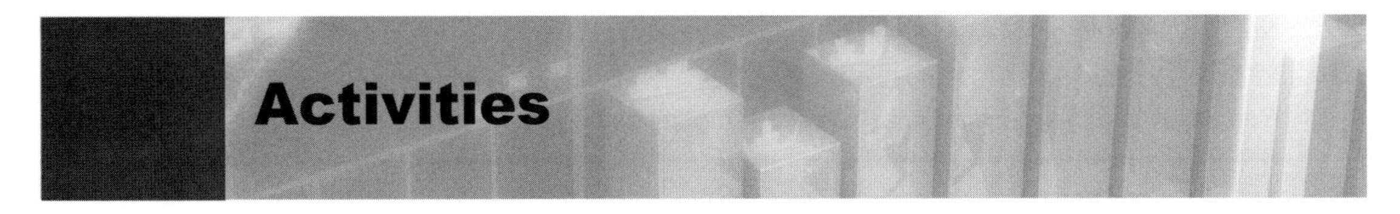

3.1 You work in the sales invoice section of Wyvern Stationery, a wholesaler. You have a small batch of invoices to process for three different customers. You are required to complete and total the invoice extracts, including trade discount and VAT as required (and rounded down).

(a) 20 box files (black), product code 109BK@ £4.00 each with 30% trade discount

(b) 90 biros (red), product code 235RD @ £5.60 per box of 10, with 20% trade discount

(c) 8 year planners (blue), product code 563BL @ £12.95 each, with 10% trade discount

(a)

product code	description	quantity	price £	unit	total £	discount %	net £
						Total VAT @ 20%	
						TOTAL	

(b)

product code	description	quantity	price £	unit	total £	discount %	net £
						Total VAT @ 20%	
						TOTAL	

(c)

product code	description	quantity	price £	unit	total £	discount %	net £
						Total VAT @ 20%	
						TOTAL	

3.2 You are working out some prices for a customer and note that some discount calculations produce results involving more than 2 decimal places.

You are to use the rounding rules to ensure that all of the following results are reduced to 2 decimal places:

(a) 15% discount on an amount of £45.50

(b) 20% discount on an amount of £44.99

(c) 30% discount on an amount of £21.75

(d) 15% discount on an amount of £390.95

(e) 30% discount on an amount of £964.55

(f) 2.5% discount on an amount of £35.95

3.3 The following amounts include VAT charged at 20%. You are to work out in each case the VAT amount and the amount before VAT was added on.

(a) £49.20

(b) £292.80

(c) £2.28

(d) £436.80

(e) £105.60

3.4 You work for Hypnos Enterprises. You have been asked to complete the following tables showing their annual sales and profit figures for the last two years. You have been asked to calculate and comment on in each case:

(a) the difference between the forecast and actual figures, noting if it is '+' or '–'

(b) the difference as a percentage of the forecast (benchmark) figure

HYPNOS ENTERPRISES – Annual Sales

	Forecast (benchmark) £	Actual £	Difference £	Percentage difference
Year 1	600,000	642,000		
Year 2	640,000	608,000		

HYPNOS ENTERPRISES – Annual Profits

	Forecast (benchmark) £	Actual £	Difference £	Percentage difference
Year 1	64,000	67,200		
Year 2	65,000	63,050		

3.5 Shown below are two pie charts based on the sales figures of Newbury Limited for Years 1 and 4.

State why you think these pie charts are not so useful in showing the year-to-year sales trends.

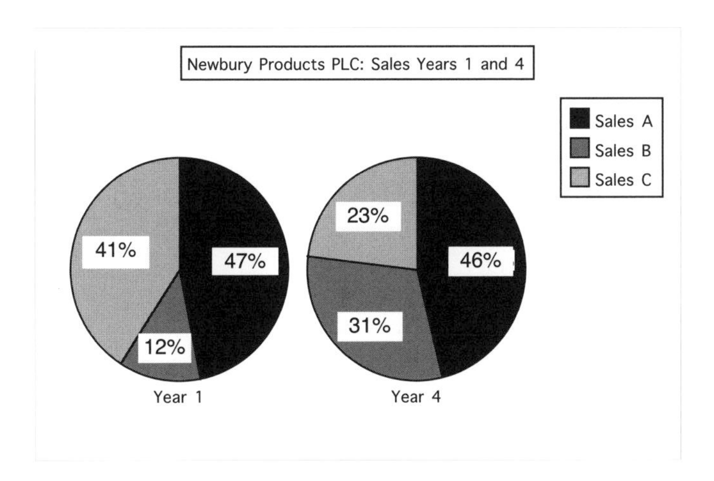

3.6 Calculate the average (mean, median and mode) hourly rate of employees' pay from the following figures:

Andy	£7.50
Bella	£7.75
Carlo	£7.80
Dirk	£7.85
Estelle	£7.90
Freddy	£9.00
Gina	£11.00
Hal	£11.00
Ian	£14.20

Which average figure are you likely to use if you are compiling a report on wage costs, and why?

4 Communication at work

this chapter covers...

This chapter explains the need for people working in accounting and finance to be able to communicate:

- *with colleagues in the workplace*
- *with people outside the workplace – customers and suppliers, for example*

This chapter will explain that

- *effective communication needs to be clear, appropriate to the situation and easily understood*
- *effective communication needs to be accurate and technically correct*
- *when communicating with outsiders, employees should project a professional image of the organisation.*
- *communication may be verbal*
- *communication may be written down by hand or processed on a computer*
- *the language used in business communications is generally more formal than everyday language used with friends and family*

The specific types of communication covered include:

- *emails*
- *memos*
- *notes*
- *faxes*
- *letters*
- *informal business reports*

THE NEED TO COMMUNICATE

the need for effective communication

We saw in the last chapter that numerical skills are particularly important in the accounting and finance workplace. In this chapter we describe the need for effective communication, a set of skills which are vital not only in the workplace but in all walks of life.

If you are communicating a message to another person or group of people, that message must be **effective** to be successful. It must achieve its aim and be:

- clear and easily understood – concise and expressed in unambiguous language
- correct – there is no point in unintentionally misleading people
- provided at the right time – not too early and not too late

On a personal level, if you are organising a meal out with a group of friends, you will need to email, phone or text instructions giving clear details of the place, date and time and asking for confirmation. You need to provide this information in good time and be available to receive replies. This is a very basic comparison, but the same principles apply to any workplace situation.

forms of communication – the people involved

Communication can be very varied. If you consider a working day and compile a log of all the forms of communication you get involved in you would find that you would be recording:

- **internal communications** – with colleagues, line managers and anyone else involved in your reporting lines
- **external communications** – depending on your role in the organisation, this could be with customers, suppliers, the bank, carriers and the local sandwich or pizza delivery company

If you are communicating **within the organisation** you should

- choose the most appropriate method
- be polite – even if you do not feel like it at the time
- act promptly – do not leave things to later, they may never happen

If you are communicating **with outsiders** you should

- choose the most appropriate method of communication
- communicate clearly, accurately and promptly
- present a professional approach
- comply with 'corporate image' – this may mean using standard letters and forms, or speaking on the telephone using standard 'scripts'

forms of communication – the methods used

There is a wide variety of methods of communication that can be used. There is normally a clear choice for most circumstances, although occasionally it can be effective if a normally accepted method is changed if the circumstances demand it. For example, a telephone call may be more effective than yet another unanswered email in dealing with a potential problem, communication being better than silence.

The choice of communication methods used involve a number of classifications:

- **verbal** or **written** methods of communication
  - telephone calls, voicemail messages, meetings, as opposed to
  - letters, memos, reports, notes
- written communication can be **paper-based** or **electronic**
  - letters, memos, notes, reports, as opposed to
  - emails, faxes, texts

The choice will normally be based on custom, ie 'what is normally done'. The skill is in choosing the most appropriate method. The variety of possible methods is shown in the diagram set out below.

In the rest of the chapter we will describe some of the more common communication methods – including emails, letters, memos and informal business reports.

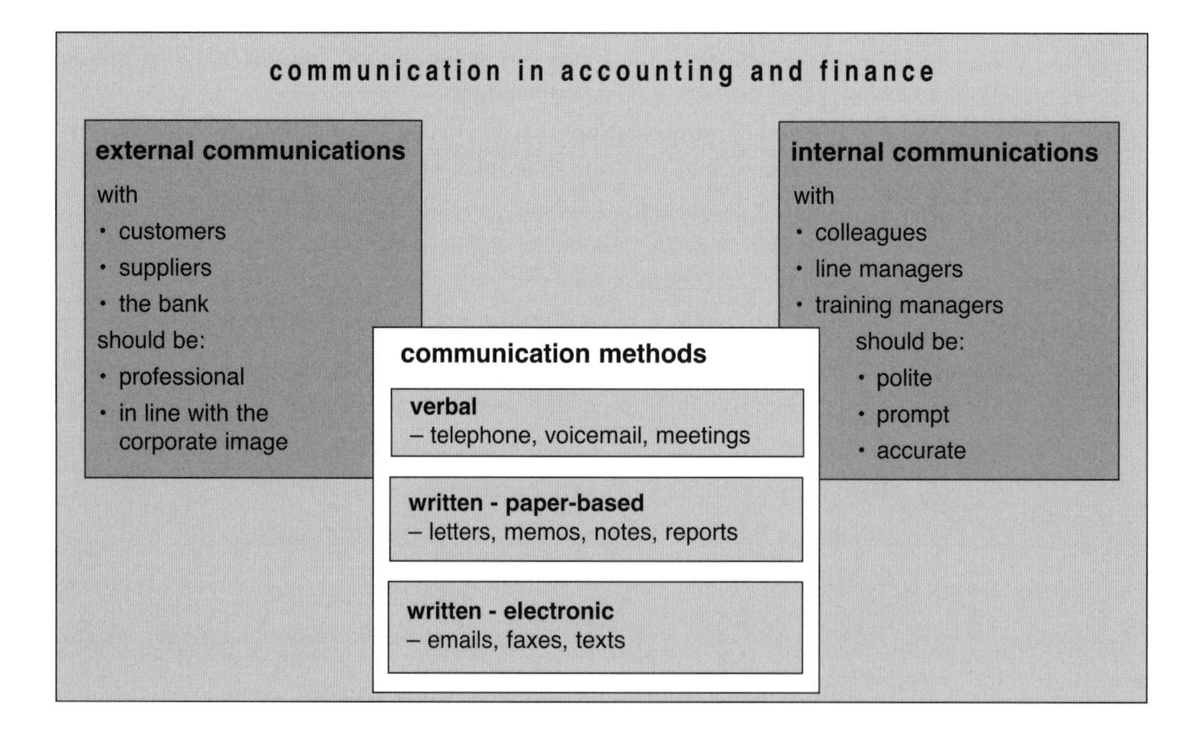

EMAILS

'netiquette' - the art of email writing

Email is a very common form of written communication. There is an established set of rules of 'what to do' and 'what not to do' when writing email. This is often referred to as 'netiquette.'If you work for an organisation you must ensure that you are familiar with the ways in which emails are written and dealt with. It is essential that you always project a professional image of your organisation when composing and replying to an email.

Although professional emails are seen as being more informal than letters, there is no excuse for careless mistakes, use of texting language, smileys, LOTS OF CAPITAL LETTERS and exclamation marks!!!!!!!

Study the email shown below and then read the hints that follow.

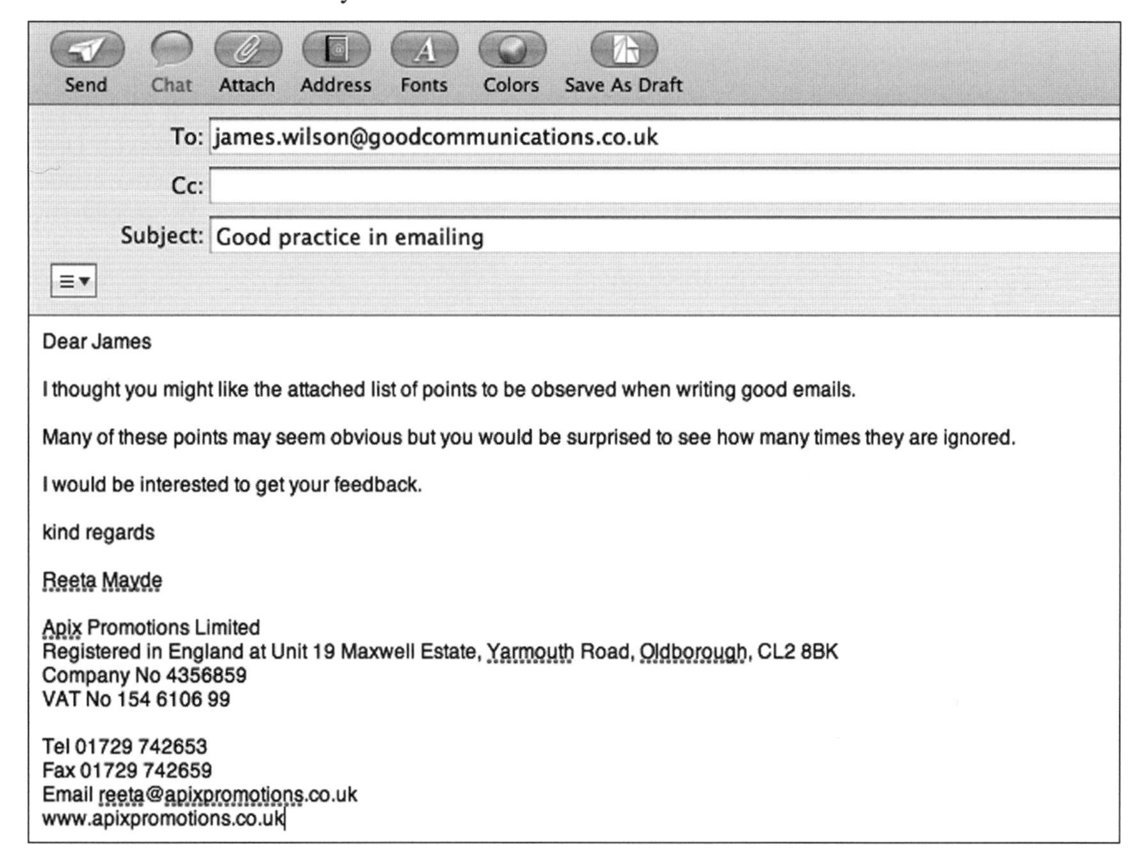

Dear James

I thought you might like the attached list of points to be observed when writing good emails.

Many of these points may seem obvious but you would be surprised to see how many times they are ignored.

I would be interested to get your feedback.

kind regards

Reeta Mayde

Apix Promotions Limited
Registered in England at Unit 19 Maxwell Estate, Yarmouth Road, Oldborough, CL2 8BK
Company No 4356859
VAT No 154 6106 99

Tel 01729 742653
Fax 01729 742659
Email reeta@apixpromotions.co.uk
www.apixpromotions.co.uk

subject

Keep the subject description short and to the point.Use a capital letter for the start of the first word.

Cc

The 'Cc' (carbon copy) is used to send a message to a group of people, and each person in the group who receives the message will see the addresses of the others in the list. These people should therefore ideally know each other. 'Cc' should only be used if you are happy that they are all aware that the others on the list are receiving the message. If it is used to send a message to a group of strangers you may annoy them and breach privacy regulations.

Bcc

'Bcc' (blind carbon copy) is an option (not shown on the illustration) which can be used to e-mail a group of contacts who do not know each other. 'Bcc' allows the message to go to a group, but the group members do not know that it is a group mailing as they do not see the details of the other recipients.

addressing the recipient

How do you address your new contacts? It all depends on the relationship. If the person is well known to you, the usual 'Hi Ramjit,' 'Hello Laura,' is quite acceptable. The approach is very similar to a telephone call. If you do not know the recipient you should be very formal: 'Dear Mr Lubowski,' 'Dear Ms. Terry,' and so on. You should remain on formal terms until in due course it is clear from the other person that you can say 'Hi Sue,' or whatever is required.

signing off

On the whole you should use the same process as you would if you were writing a business letter. If you start with 'Dear Mr Brown' you should finish with 'Yours sincerely' although there is a tendency now also to use 'kind regards' or 'best wishes' instead.

how formal should the text be?

A business email is not an informal communication. Remember that your message represents the public front of the organisation which employs you. It should have correct spelling, grammar and punctuation. Sentences should be short and separated into distinct paragraphs.

It helps if you put a blank line between paragraphs.

some do's and don'ts

Do . . .

- keep the message short and to the point
- when replying, answer the points raised in the incoming message

- reply or confirm receipt of the message on the same day
- read through and edit what you have written before you send it
- make sure the original message 'thread' is included if you are replying

Do not . . .

- use text in CAPITAL LETTERS - THIS IS KNOWN AS 'SHOUTING'
- use too much fancy formatting, eg underlines, different fonts, bright colours – they may be lost when the message is printed out by the recipient
- send large attachments which might clog up the recipient's email system
- say something in an email that you would not say to someone's face

the proper approach

Remember a good email and the three P's:

- prompt
- polite
- professional

The next form of communication we will describe is the **memorandum**, a paper-based internal document which has nowadays largely been superseded by the internal email.

THE MEMORANDUM

format

The **memorandum** (plural memoranda) is a formal written note used for internal communication within an organisation. It may be word-processed or handwritten, and will often be produced in a number of copies which can be circulated as necessary. A memorandum may be sent by email within an organisation.

A memorandum can be used for situations such as:

- giving instructions
- requesting information
- making suggestions
- recording of opinions
- confirming telephone conversations

A memorandum is normally pre-printed by the organisation with all the headings in place, and can be half page or full page in size (see next page).

elements of the memorandum

'to' and 'from'	the name and job title of the sender and the recipient are entered in full, and the formal phrases you find on letters, eg 'Dear......' and 'Yours ....' are not necessary
copies to	memoranda are sometimes sent to a number of people; the recipients will be indicated in this section of the document
subject	the subject matter of the memorandum must be stated concisely
text	the message of the memorandum should be clear and concise
signature	a memorandum can be signed, initialled, or even – as is often the case – left blank
enclosures	if material is circulated with the memorandum, the abbreviation 'enc' or 'encl' should be used

MEMORANDUM

To John Stone, Accounts Supervisor

From Tim Blake, Sales Manager **Ref** TB/AC/1098

Copies to n/a **Date** 23 June 20-3

Subject Bad payers

Please can you let me have an updated list of our customers who exceed their credit period and pay late.

I need to give this list to the sales reps so that they will not be tempted to extend credit any further to these customers.

Thank you.

a completed memorandum relating to customer accounts

THE NOTE

One of the most common forms of communication within an organisation is the **note**. This can be:

- an informal written note, passing on a message or an instruction
- a telephone message (some organisations use preprinted telephone message pads)

The important elements of a written note are

- the name of the person who is sending the note
- the name of the person who is to receive the note
- the time and date that the note is written
- a clearly stated message
- a clear indication of any action to be taken as a result of the message

Examine the examples set out below and see how they contain all these elements.

To Tim Blackstock,
Order Processing

Please remember to allow PDT Ltd an extra 10% trade discount on invoices this month.

John Tregennick, Sales
03.04.-3 10.30

TELEPHONE MESSAGE

TO Karin Schmidt, Accounts
FROM H Khan, Sales
DATE 22 April 20-3
TIME 12.30

Please ring Jim Stoat at RF Electronics - he is complaining that they have not received a credit note for returned damaged inventory (order ref 823423).

Please treat urgently - he is not very happy!

HK

THE FAX

The fax (short for 'facsimile') enables you to transmit electronically an exact copy of the details on a sheet of paper. This can either be done on a computer or on a fax machine. If you use a fax machine you feed the sheet into the machine, dial up the recipient on the inbuilt telephone pad and transmit the document down the line. The machine at the other end will print out an exact copy of the original document.

The fax can be used within an organisation or for external contact with a customer. You normally send a 'fax header' first sheet (see illustration below) and then feed in any further pages/documents as required.

The fax is very useful for sending copies of documents. A frequent excuse given by people who are slow at paying is "I can't pay because I don't seem to have the original invoice". This can be replied to with 'No problem! We can fax you a copy. What is your fax number?' Look at the example below.

Winterborn Electronics Limited

Unit 4 Everoak Estate, Bromyard Road
St Johns, Worcester WR2 5HN
tel 01905 748043 fax 01905 748911

facsimile transmission header

To: Jamie Milne, Accounts Office, Zippo Computers

Fax number: 01350 525504

Number of pages including this header: 2 Date: 17 October 20-3

message

Invoice 24375

Further to our recent telephone conversation I am faxing you a copy of invoice 24375 which is now overdue.

I shall be grateful if you will arrange for the £4,678.50 owing to be paid to us as soon as possible.

R Pound

Credit Controller

THE 'HOUSE STYLE' LETTER

When you deal with business letters you will see that the appearance and format of each letter is in a uniform 'house' style, a style which identifies that business, and is common to all letters that it sends. The letter will normally be on standard printed stationery showing the name, address and details of the business, and will be set out with headings, paragraphs, signatures – the 'elements' of the letter – in a uniform way.

There are a number of different ways of setting out the text of a letter. The most common of these – the 'fully blocked' style – is illustrated and explained on the next two pages.

characteristics of a fully blocked letter

- the most commonly used style of letter
- all the lines start at the left margin
- the use of open punctuation, ie there is no punctuation, except in the main body of the letter, which uses normal punctuation
- paragraphs are divided by a space, and are not indented
- a fully blocked letter is easy to key in as all the lines are set uniformly to the left margin

elements of the letter

The explanations which follow refer to the illustration of the letter on page 67.

printed letterhead The name and address of the business is normally pre-printed, and must be up-to-date.

reference The reference on the letter illustrated – DH/SB/69 – is a standard format

- DH (Derek Hunt), the writer
- SB (Sally Burgess), the secretary
- 69, the number of the file where the correspondence is kept

If you need to quote the reference of a letter to which you are replying, the references will be quoted as follows: Your ref TR/FG/45 Our ref DH/SB/69.

date — The date is typed in date (number), month (word), year (number) order.

recipient — The name and address of the person to whom the letter is sent. This section of the letter may be displayed in the window of a window envelope, so it is essential that it is accurate.

salutation — 'Dear Sir. . . Dear Madam' – if you know the person's name and title (ie Mr, Mrs, Miss, Ms) use it, but check that it is correct – a misspelt name or an incorrect title will ruin an otherwise competent letter.

heading — The heading sets out the subject matter of the letter – it will concentrate the reader's mind.

body — The body of the letter is an area where the message of the letter is set out. The text must:

- be laid out in short precise paragraphs and short clear sentences
- start with a point of reference (eg referring to an invoice)
- set out the message in a logical sequence
- be written in plain English – but avoid 'slang' expressions and, equally, avoid unusual or old-fashioned words which obscure the meaning
- finish with a clear indication of the next step to be taken (eg please telephone, please arrange appointment, please buy our products, please pay our invoice)

complimentary close — The complimentary close (signing off phrase) must be consistent with the salutation:

'Dear Sir/Dear Madam' followed by 'Yours faithfully'

'Dear Mr Sutton/Dear Ms Jones' followed by 'Yours sincerely'.

name and job title — It is essential for the reader to know the name of the person who sent the letter, and that person's job title, because a reply will need to be addressed to a specific person.

enclosures — If there are enclosures with the letter, the abbreviation 'enc' or 'encl' is used at the bottom of the letter.

the 'house style' letter

reference →	Ref DH/SB/69
date →	15 December 20-3
name and address of recipient →	Purchasing Department Osborne Car Accessories 17 Pump Street Mereford MR6 7ER
salutation →	Dear Sir
heading →	Invoice 8288 £10,589.50
body of the letter →	We note from our records that we have not yet received payment of our invoice 8288 dated 15 September 20-3. Our up-to-date statement of account is enclosed, together with a copy of the invoice. Our payment terms are strictly 30 days from the date of the invoice. We shall be grateful if you will settle the £10,589.50 without further delay. We look forward to receiving your cheque.
complimentary close →	Yours faithfully
signature →	*D M Hunt*
name and job title →	Derek Hunt Accounts Manager
enclosures →	enc

Letterhead:

Wyvern Motor Supplies
107 High Street
Mereford
MR1 9SZ
Tel 01605 675365 Fax 01605 765576

THE INFORMAL REPORT

who needs written reports?

A written report is a way of informing someone about a specific subject. A report is a structured way of communicating complex information. Reports can be short or extended, formal or informal.

A **formal report** is commonly used in business to investigate, discuss and decide on specific **policy** issues, for example an assessment of changes to the accounting system, the paying of bonuses, the possibility of exporting products. A formal report may be prepared for a business by outside consultants, or by people within a business for the attention of senior management.

Formal reports normally have a complex structure:

- Title Page
- Terms of reference
- Procedure
- Findings
- Conclusions
- Recommendations
- Appendices

An **informal report,** on the other hand, is a format often used in business to communicate **routine** matters – facts or results rather than opinions – within the same department or to another department, for example:

- a report of sales figures prepared by the accounts department for the sales managers
- a report of overtime worked over six months by employees prepared for the accounts department

Informal reports have a much simpler structure:

- Title and date
- Introduction
- Findings
- Conclusions and recommendations (optional)

We will describe each of these sections of an informal report in turn.

title and date

The informal report will normally be headed up with

- the person it is sent to (plus job title)
- the person who has prepared the report (plus job title)
- the date
- the title of the report

For example:

> To: Josh Khan, Accounts Manager
>
> From: A Student, Accounts Assistant, Sales Ledger
>
> Date: 5 February 20-3
>
> REPORT ON POSSIBLE BAD DEBT WRITE-OFFS

introduction

This will state:

- the nature of the task set and the date when it was set
- the person who set the task (normally the person to whom it is sent)
- the deadline for the task

Using the example shown above, this might read:

> **1. Introduction**
>
> 1.1 On 30 January I was requested by you to investigate any sales ledger accounts that were outstanding for more than two months later than the due date and to provide you with a list and details of all overdue amounts. This was so that you could assess them for possible bad debt write-off.
>
> 1.2 This was to be completed by 7 February.

Note that the decimal system of numbering is used. This means that the first section of the informal report is the Introduction and

- it is given the identifying number '1'
- the sub-sections of the Introduction are referenced with the numbers '1.1' and '1.2'. If there had been a third it would have been '1.3'

findings

The second section of the informal report contains the 'Findings.' This will set out all the information that you gathered together as a result of your investigation. You should briefly list your sources of information and then set out your findings in a clear and logical way.

You could use a table to set out your data (see page 45 in the 'Working with numbers' chapter), and if requested or appropriate, you could produce a graph or chart to illustrate your data. If you are using a computer spreadsheet program such as Excel, this would give a more professional appearance to what you are doing. If your findings included a lot of data or printouts, you could possibly put them in an Appendix and refer to them in the main text.

The 'Findings' of the possible bad debt report used as an example on the previous page may start off as shown below. Note the use of the number '2' and '2.1' and '2.2' to provide a referencing system for the report.

2. Findings

2.1 The information gathered for this report was taken from

- the Sales Ledger accounts
- the Aged Debtor Analysis Report for January

It also includes copies of relevant correspondence relating to the overdue accounts.

2.2 The list showing the overdue accounts and the amounts involved is as follows

. . . (here you would insert an appropriate table)

conclusions and recommendations

This section is not often found in an informal report. More often than not informal reports just provide facts and figures and do not give opinions or recommendations.

It is possible, however, that a conclusion and recommendations are requested, especially if the person compiling the report has some responsibility for the subject being reported. As a general rule, opinions or recommendations should not been given unless requested.

If a conclusion and recommendations are given, they should be based entirely on the 'Findings' and should not introduce any other factors or information. This section of the report could begin as follows:

3. Conclusion and recommendations

3.1 Based on the figures and the correspondence in the Findings, I draw the conclusion that it is unlikely that we will be able to recover the following customer debts:

. . . (a list of accounts and amounts would be entered)

3.2 My recommendation is that these debts should be written off as bad debts in the accounts.

a written or word-processed informal report?

Although it is possible to hand-write an informal report, modern office practice is likely to favour a word-processed document:

- it is clearer
- it can be stored and sent more easily
- it can easily incorporate tables and charts
- it looks more professional
- it can act as a template if the report is a regular event – for example, a monthly sales analysis

what style of language should be used?

A report requires straightforward written English. There is nothing particularly difficult about producing written English; the problems lie with the current tendency to write as you speak, or as you text, or as you email. The result is often an abbreviated form of written English which as you will appreci8 does nt work 2 well on the page.

Another problem facing people who are not used to writing formal written English is that they think of it as some sort of overblown 'posh' sounding language which has to be complicated and impressive to make its point. Nothing could be further from the truth. The test of good written English is that it should be plain and simple.

some hints on writing plain English in a report

- use **simple words** instead of complicated ones
- use **short sentences** instead of long ones
- split up the text into manageable **paragraphs**

- use the **active tense** rather than the passive, eg 'the line manager *carries out* regular checks on the petty cash book' rather than 'regular checks *are carried out* on the petty cash book by the line manager'
- **avoid slang** eg 'the manager was really *hacked off*'; you should use the word 'annoyed' instead of 'hacked' to avoid the innocent reader assuming that the manager has suffered some terrible injury
- avoid **abbreviations** such as 'isn't', didn't' and write the phrases in full: 'is not' and 'did not'

informal reports – conclusion

Writing a report – formal or informal – can sometimes seem a daunting prospect, simply because reports are longer and more complex than any other form of business communication.

In fact reports are straightforward because they are very structured. All you have to do is to:

- comply with the report brief – ie write about what has been requested
- observe the formatting requirements – ie the various sections, suitably numbered
- keep the subject matter and language simple and concise
- provide tables and charts as required
- check carefully what you have written
- hand it in on time

Chapter Summary

- Effective **communication** is essential to the efficient running of an organisation. Any message must be easily understood, correct and communicated on time.
- Communication in an organisation can be **internal** (with colleagues) and **external** (eg with customers). It is important that all external communications, whatever the format, give a **professional image** of the organisation.
- There are many different types of communication, all used for very specific purposes, for example:
  - verbal and written communications
  - paper-based and electronic communications
- The main **verbal communications** are telephone and voicemail messages, and discussions in meetings.
- The main **written communications** are letters, memos, notes and reports (all paper-based) and emails and faxes (electronic messages).

email an increasingly popular form of electronic communication with a unique set of procedures, different from letter writing.

netiquette the rules for writing emails which must be strictly observed if an organisation is to maintain a professional 'corporate' image

memorandum a formal paper-based internal message (often called a 'memo') which can be used for a wide variety of communications, ranging from simple instructions to informal reports; the memorandum is rapidly being superseded by the email

note a simple written message used within an organisation to pass on information or make a request

fax the process in which a paper document is scanned and sent electronically to the recipient

business letter a formal paper document, drawn up in a specific 'house style,' used for a wide range of purposes and normally posted to the recipient

informal report an internal document which is normally used for routine purposes for sending factual information requested by the recipient; it rarely involves any form of opinion or recommendation

Activities

4.1 Which of the following four options is the most important for creating an effective communication?

(a) the message must be clear and in writing

(b) the message must be clear and correct

(c) the message must be clear and on time

(d) the message must be clear, correct and on time

4.2 You work as an accounts assistant in the sales ledger section of the accounts department of Excelsium Sports, a wholesaler of sports equipment. During the course of a working day you encounter a number of situations which require you to communicate a response to a message or a problem.

You are to choose for each situation the most suitable form of communication from the following list:

fax, email, internal note, voicemail, memorandum

You are then to:

(a) Explain in each case why the form of communication you have chosen provides the most effective solution.

(b) Draft the text of the message you would use to reply to each. If a document (including email) is involved, you do not have to incorporate the heading. Use your own name. The date is 11 July 20-3.

situations

1 You receive a telephone call for Neeta, a colleague who sits at the desk next to you. She is out at lunch. The call is from a customer, John Maxwell, who is querying a credit note (No 5242) sent out by Neeta. John says that it is not urgent, but he would appreciate a call in the afternoon, after 3.00 pm. His telephone number is 077195648012.

2 James Greenap, who deals with the accounts at Protosport, a local sports shop, leaves a message for you with your colleague Neeta. He cannot find invoice 29082 for £595.50 dated 25 June 20-3 which appears on his latest statement. He urgently requires a copy. Neeta has told him that you will send him a copy when you return.

3 You have been asked by the Accounts Manager to circulate around the office staff a printed menu from the local Italian restaurant for the staff pizza and pasta social night on 31 July, asking for names of people who want to go. She wants to know the menu choices in advance, by 20 July at the latest.

4 You receive an email from a customer, Jetstream Sports, addressed to the Accounts Department complaining that a recent invoice only gave 20% trade discount on goods costing £200 and what were you going to do about it? You refer to the customer list and see that the normal discount given is 30%. You refer the matter to the Accounts Manager who asks you to apologise by return and offer an adjusting credit note.

5 You telephone a customer, Zenith Kit Ltd, to query a purchase order received from them. They have ordered 25 Bradville United football team shirts (product code BU546) but have quoted the product code BT546 which relates to Bradfield Town football team shirts. When you telephone them, you hear a recorded message:

"This is Zenith Kit Ltd. We are sorry but we are unable to take your call at the moment. Please leave a message after the tone. Thank you."

4.3 You are an experienced accounts assistant in the sales ledger section of the accounts department of Excelsium Sports. You are currently helping to train Nico, a new member of staff. This week he is helping to prepare standard letters for sending out to customers who are late in settling their accounts. The letters are for signature by Ann Dover, your Credit Controller. He passes you two letters for checking.

You are to check the two letters for mistakes and state what you think is wrong with them.

(a)

Excelsium Sports

Witley Road, St Gregorys, MR1 5GT
Tel 01908 675234 Fax 01908 675332 email info@excelsiumsports.co.uk

The Manager, Accounts Department
Speedo Importers Limited
Henman Road
Silvertown
SY3 7YH

Dear Sir

Account 29244

We note from our records that we have not yet received settlement of our invoices totalling £764.50 Our invoice terms are strictly 30 days and these items are now overdue.

We shall be grateful if you will kindly settle this amount by return of post.

Yours sincerely

Ann Dover
Credit Controller

(b)

Excelsium Sports

Witley Road, St Gregorys, MR1 5GT
Tel 01908 675234 Fax 01908 675332 email info@excelsiumsports.co.uk

4 August 20-3

Dear Mr Major

Account 10936

Further to our previous reminders we still have not received settlement of the overdue invoices on your account. We shall be grateful if you will kindly forward us your cheque for £1546.88. If this amount has not been received at this address within seven working days we will have no alternative but to place the matter in the hands of our solicitors.

Yours faithfully

Ann Dover
Credit Controller

5 Working independently in an organisation

this chapter covers...

This chapter explains the need for a person working in an organisation to be able to work independently as an individual in order to help to achieve the objectives of the organisation.

The principles set out here apply not just to the accounting and finance function but to all areas of the organisation.

An employee working as an individual must be able to:

- *work effectively and efficiently to achieve the objectives set by the organisation*
- *work in line with the procedures set out by the organisation*
- *manage the workload by identifying the different types of task involved*
- *prioritise these tasks and meet deadlines that have been set*
- *use appropriate planning aids such as diaries, 'to do' lists, action plans and schedules to help with this process*
- *know what to do if things do not go to plan, priorities change and rescheduling becomes necessary*
- *communicate with management when things go wrong*
- *maintain confidentiality at all times*

The next chapter then explains what is required of the individual as a member of a team in the workplace – the need to communicate well and to be able to cope with conflicts that can arise between team members.

THE INDIVIDUAL AND THE ORGANISATION

work and family

Employees normally come to work, not just to earn money, but because the workplace, like a family, is a social grouping of people who work and socialise together. By going to work, employees gain a unique sense of identity which the organisation and social grouping provides. The idea of the workplace as an extended 'family' or 'team' was promoted over a hundred years ago in Birmingham, UK, by Cadbury's, the chocolate manufacturer.

Employees in this way learn to treat the workplace as an environment in which they have a sense of responsibility for what they do, for example:

- the everyday tasks that they have to carry out
- the idea that they are working together to achieve common objectives set by the organisation

working effectively and efficiently

What exactly do these two terms mean?

'Effective' means getting the result that you want. In football an effective defence prevents the opposing team scoring goals, in the dating game an effective chat-up line will win you the partner you have your eye on. An **effective working environment** will result in the achievement of the objectives of the organisation, for example – a motivated workforce, sales and profit targets achieved or exceeded.

'Efficient' is not the same as 'effective'. It means getting the job done with the minimum waste of effort and resources. This is, of course, an important objective in any organisation. But note that an **efficient working environment** will not always be 'effective'. A line manager, for example, may be ruthlessly efficient in saving time and money, but the workforce may be fed up with her to the extent that levels of performance will fall off. The working environment will become less 'effective'.

The ideal working environment, therefore, is one that **balances effectiveness and efficiency**. The job is done well with the minimum wastage of effort and resources.

employees and objectives

What are the 'objectives' of an organisation referred to at the top of this page? They may well include:

- customer satisfaction – making the customer the main focus of the organisation

- profitability – which should benefit employees, owners and customers
- being environmentally friendly – reducing wastage of natural resources, eg energy and paper

In order to achieve these objectives, organisations promote:

- customer care schemes
- profit-sharing schemes
- 'green' schemes to cut down on wastage, eg of energy and paper

These objectives can affect the way employees are required to carry out their day-to-day tasks.

The example below shows how a Customer Care scheme in a major financial services company sets very specific targets for the performance of workplace tasks. When an assistant sorts out a customer query, it is not just a case of 'that's another one out of the way' but 'I got a buzz of satisfaction in showing that our organisation cares about its customers.'

day-to-day tasks in a Customer Care scheme

efficiency

- aim to be 100% error free
- answer all letters within 2 days of receipt
- advise customers of delivery timescales

problem solving

- take ownership – don't blame others
- resolve complaints within 2 to 10 working days
- follow up afterwards to ensure that the customer is satisfied

courtesy

- greet customers and smile
- use customer's name
- give customer 100% of your attention

dealing with customers who are waiting

- serve all customers within 4 minutes
- apologise if a customer is kept waiting
- make visible efforts to reduce waiting times

using the telephone

- answer before the third ring, if possible
- speak clearly to customers, use their name and check their understanding of what you say

organisational procedures

The way in which employees tackle tasks is often set down in written sets of **procedures**. Larger organisations are likely to have manuals which give guidance; smaller organisations may have written 'checklists' compiled by experienced staff. Examples of jobs in an accounting context which will have set procedures for the tasks carried out include:

- supermarket cashiers dealing with cash, debit and credit cards
- employees processing payroll
- accounts assistants paying customer invoices

The example shown below is a set of procedures for a shop taking payment by debit and credit card using a 'chip and pin' system.

cashier procedures for taking 'chip and pin' payment by debit and credit card

- Insert the card in the card reader, or ask the customer to do so.
- Confirm the amount of the transaction with the customer.
- Ask the customer to insert his/her four digit 'PIN' number.
- Ensure that you are not watching the customer enter the number.
- Ensure that nobody else is watching the customer enter the number.
- If the card is 'locked' at the till, ie the wrong number has been entered three times, the customer should be advised to contact the card company. The customer should be asked to provide an alternative form of payment.
- The terminal will tell you if the PIN transaction is successful or has been declined.
- At the end of the transaction hand the receipt (and the card if you have it) to the customer.
- Always ensure the customer has the card in his/her possession when leaving the till.

the need to prioritise

So far in this chapter we have seen that an employee normally has sets of instructions and procedures to learn when doing a job. The day-to-day work will involve a wide variety of tasks competing for the employee's time. These may be routine or non-routine, urgent or non-urgent. The employee must develop the skills needed to identify and prioritise the tasks that need to be done. We will now examine the techniques and aids available to the employee to help with this.

WHAT ARE MY TASKS?

keeping to the job description

An employee needs to know:

- what tasks need to be done in the office
- what tasks the employee is able to do in the office

These are not necessarily the same. Employees should be given a **job description** which sets out exactly what the employee is expected to be able to do. It may be that a line manager puts pressure onto an employee to carry out tasks which the employee is not qualified or able to do. The employee may think 'promotion here we come!' but also may get in a mess and make mistakes for which he or she should not really be held responsible.

One golden rule is therefore to look at your job description and know what you have to do and what limits there are to your range of activities.

identifying types of tasks

The next golden rule is to be able to identify exactly what tasks have to be done and to identify what type of tasks they are, because this will affect the order in which you will carry them out.

There are a number of different types of task, for example, in an accounts office . . .

- **routine tasks**

  These are everyday tasks such as reading the post and emails, checking invoices, inputting data, sending standard letters, answering telephone queries, photocopying and filing. They do not hold any great surprises, but their efficient completion is important to the smooth running of the office.

- **non-routine tasks**

  These are the unexpected tasks such as helping with one-off projects, working out of the office on a special assignment, or helping to clear up after the washroom has flooded. These may hold up your normal routine work.

Routine tasks are easy to plan for because they are predictable.

Non-routine tasks cannot be planned for, and they can sometimes cause problems, as we will see later in the chapter. They call for flexibility and logical thinking, skills which can be developed over time.

As you will know some people thrive on routine and do not like it to be upset; others get bored by it and enjoy the challenges of the unexpected.

In addition, tasks may be **urgent** and they may be **important**. These are not always the same thing . . .

- **urgent tasks**

  These are tasks which have to be done by a specific pressing deadline: the manager may need a spreadsheet immediately for a meeting currently taking place; customer statements may have to go out in tonight's post.

- **important tasks**

  These are tasks for which you have been given personal responsibility. They may be part of your normal routine and other people depend on their successful completion, or they may have been delegated to you because your line manager thinks you are capable of completing them.

working out the priorities

Prioritising tasks means deciding the order of the tasks. Which one first? Which one last? Which tasks matter? Which tasks do not matter so much? The two main factors involved in the decision are **urgency** and **importance**.

The guide to the basic order of priority is shown below. You may, of course, think of exceptions to this rule, particularly with items 2 and 3.

an order of priority . . .

1	Tasks that are **urgent and important** – they have got to be done soon and if you do not do them you are going to let a lot of people down – eg producing the spreadsheet for the manager's meeting.
2	Tasks that are **urgent but less important**, eg watering office plants which have dried out – if you fail to water them straightaway the job still needs doing, but the office is not going to grind to a halt if they remain dry.
3	Tasks that are **important but not urgent**, eg producing some sales figures for your line manager for a meeting at the end of the week – the task has to be done, but it could be done tomorrow.
4	Tasks that are **neither important nor urgent**, eg archiving material from some old files. This task is a useful 'filler' when the office becomes less busy; but it would not matter if it were put off for a week or two.

Case Study

FLICK'S DAY – WORKING OUT THE PRIORITIES

Flick works as an accounts assistant at the Liverpool head office of Estro PLC, a company that makes vacuum cleaners. Her main job is to process the incoming sales orders. She is supervised by her line manager Josie Khan.

She is not having a good week and seems stressed by the workload she has been given. It is Thursday 6 February and things are getting no better.

She has written down her tasks on various bits of paper and has stuck post-it notes on the side of her computer screen, marking them 'Remember!' Her colleague, Kirsty, has written notes to her. She also has her daily routine sheet which came with her job description.

These are all shown below.

SALES ORDER PROCESSING: DAILY ROUTINE

1 Collect mail, open, sort and refer where necessary
2 Open email and deal with queries - refer where necessary
3 Check incoming sales orders and debit notes
4 Check sales orders with credit control lists
5 Batch and process sales orders on computer
6 Print sales invoices and credit notes
7 Check printed documents
8 Agree batch total with computer day book summary
9 Pass invoices and credit notes for checking against order documentation
10 File copy invoices, credit notes and order documentation
11 Answer customer queries - refer where necessary

These are the notes received from Kirsty, a colleague:

Flick - Accounts Manager wants January sales figures asap!

Kirsty 6 Feb
9.30

Flick - we are moving the computers at 2.00 Thursday afternoon - can you help? Kirsty

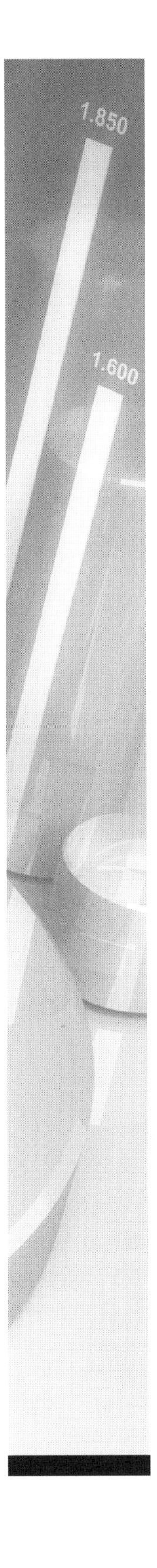

These are the 'Remember!' post-it notes Flick has stuck on the side of her computer screen:

REMEMBER!
Get instant coffee for staff kitchen. Ordinary and decaff! Both jars now empty.

REMEMBER!
4 FEB
Josie wants printouts of top 10 customer activity reports by end of Friday.

REMEMBER!
Old customer sales files need moving to separate filing drawer some time.

How is Flick going to work out her priorities?

solution

Flick takes a short morning break to discuss her various tasks with her line manager, Josie. At Josie's suggestion she thinks about the priorities involved and classifies the tasks according to how urgent they are and how important they are. She starts by prioritising the non-routine/unexpected tasks:

urgent and important tasks

- The Accounts Manager wants the January sales figures straightaway.
- The computers have to be moved at 2.00 pm that day.

urgent and less important tasks

- The staff kitchen needs more coffee.

important and non-urgent tasks

- The top 10 customer activity reports are required for Friday.

less important and non-urgent tasks

- The old customer sales files need moving to a separate filing drawer.

The non-routine tasks are fairly easily prioritised, as seen above, although there was some uncertainty over whether the staff coffee or the customer printouts had greater priority! But Flick's problem was how to combine the non-routine tasks with the big pile of routine paperwork she had to get through that day. Then there was the filing to do and customers on the telephone with 'stupid' queries.

Josie, her line manager, suggests that she should deal with her tasks in the following order:

1. urgent and important tasks – the January sales figures, shifting the computers
2. important routine tasks – these include processing and checking documentation, answering customer queries
3. urgent and less important tasks – it will not take long to get some more coffee
4. important and non-urgent tasks – the printouts for the next day (Friday)
5. less important and non-urgent tasks – filing (daily filing and shifting old files)

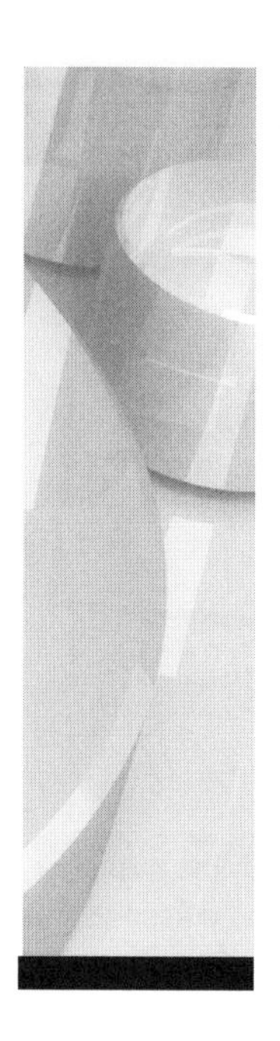

Josie also suggests that Flick compiles a prioritised 'To Do' list of all her non-routine tasks. She can then tick off the items as she does them. This will replace all the notes and Post-it stickers she has all over her desk. It can also be updated as she is asked to carry out new non-routine tasks.

FLICK'S 'TO DO' LIST

1 January sales figures for the Accounts Manager.

2 Thursday 2.00 pm move computers.

3 Coffee - get jars of ordinary and decaff at lunch time.

4 Print out top 10 customer activity reports for Josie, Friday.

5 Move old customer sales files to new drawer, as and when.

USING PLANNING AIDS

The Case Study on the last few pages has shown how an employee has become more effective by becoming more organised and prioritising tasks. The Post-it notes are important in the process, but they are only a start. There are a number of planning aids available to help with organisation, time planning and prioritisation. These include:

- a 'To Do' list – as seen above
- a diary
- a planning schedule
- an action plan

'To Do' lists

Making lists of things 'to do' is very common both at work and at home, ranging from the type of list shown above to the very basic family shopping list. It is the organised person, however, who writes these lists on an ongoing basis, possibly daily, incorporating actions which have not been ticked off on the previous day in a new list. In other words, tasks that have not been done are carried forward onto a new list. Lists may be written on paper or they may be compiled on the computer as a form of electronic 'Post-it' note.

'To do' lists may be subdivided to show the priorities of the tasks to be done. Look at the example below.

'TO DO' LIST	1 April
urgent stuff	
1 Aged debtors schedules for the Accounts Manager for today.	
2 Sales summaries for Costings section for today.	
3 Get March statements in the post today.	
non-urgent	
1 Print out activity reports for overseas customers.	
2 Set up spreadsheet for regional sales analysis.	
3 Look into venues for staff evening out.	

diaries

The diary organises tasks in terms of time. They are very useful planning aids and ensure – if they are efficiently kept – that tasks and events do not clash. Diaries can be paper-based or electronic. They can be individual diaries or office or 'section' diaries used for a group of employees.

The traditional paper-based diary with a week to view can be used alongside 'To do' lists as an efficient way of time planning and prioritising. Some people keep the 'To do' lists in their diary. The diary shown below is kept by a line manager.

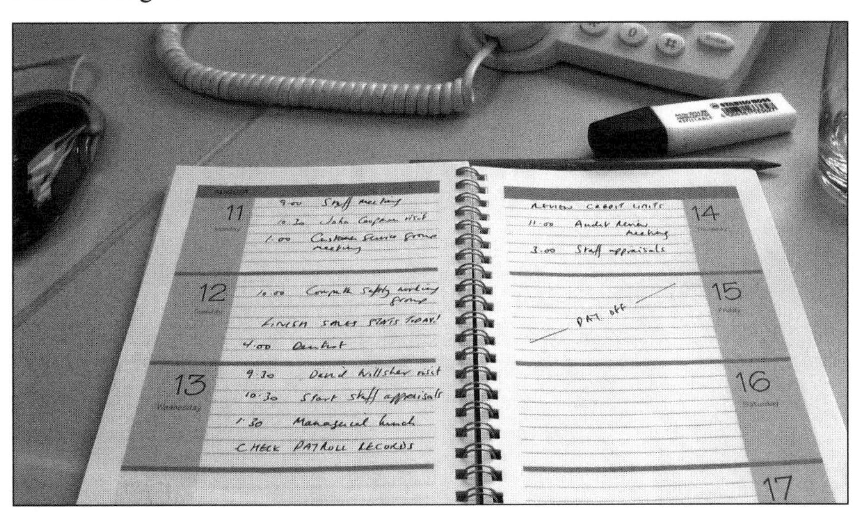

planning schedules

Planning schedules are rather more complex planning devices which deal with situations such as projects where:

- some tasks *have to* follow on from each other – to give a simple example, you have to boil the water before making a cup of coffee – these are known as **critical** activities; you cannot achieve what you want without doing them in sequence
- some tasks are **non-critical** – they are important, but the timing is not so crucial – you will have to put coffee in the cup, but you can do it while the kettle is boiling or even the day before if you want!

So whether you are making coffee or planning a space launch, the principles remain the same. Sometimes there will be a non-routine activity in the workplace, which is complicated and involves a number of inter-dependent tasks. Organisations often use a visual representation of the tasks in the form of horizontal bars set against a time scale to help with the planning. These can be drawn up manually, or, more often these days, on the computer screen using dedicated software.

It is very unlikely that you will be involved in planning a project in this way, but you may well have to interpret a chart to see how you or your section will be involved, and when. The Case Study below shows what happens when an office relocates.

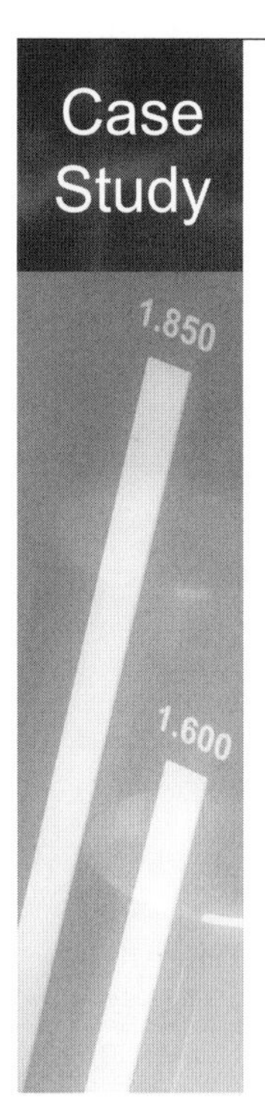

HERMES BUREAU: A PLANNING SCHEDULE

situation

You work for a computer bureau – Hermes Bureau – which provides accounting, payroll and other computer services to a wide range of commercial customers.

The business plans to invest in new premises shortly, and has purchased the lease of an office in the town, and will be able to move in six months' time.

The management of Hermes is taking the opportunity when moving to update its computer hardware and software systems.

There are a number of important tasks to carry out before the business moves, and the management has drawn up the list set out on the next page. The software needs updating and customising by programmers, and this will be the task which will take the most time. You see that all the tasks will have to be completed before the new office can become operational, and the obvious fact that the ordering of software and hardware can only take place after full assessment. The management allows itself a clear two week planning period before starting the process.

Hermes is very busy at the moment. When should the planning start?

Task A	time available for detailed planning	2 weeks
Task B	assessment of computer hardware	2 weeks
Task C	ordering new computers	2 weeks
Task D	assessment of new software	4 weeks
Task E	ordering software	10 weeks
Task F	obtaining quotes from removal firm	3 weeks
Task G	ordering the removal van	3 weeks

solution

The planning schedule drawn up by Hermes Bureau shows:

- the activities on a weekly schedule (the weeks are numbered across the top)
- the critical activities as black bars
- the activities which are not critical as grey bars
- float times for non-critical activities – ie times during which a delay can occur which will not hold up the project – as white bars

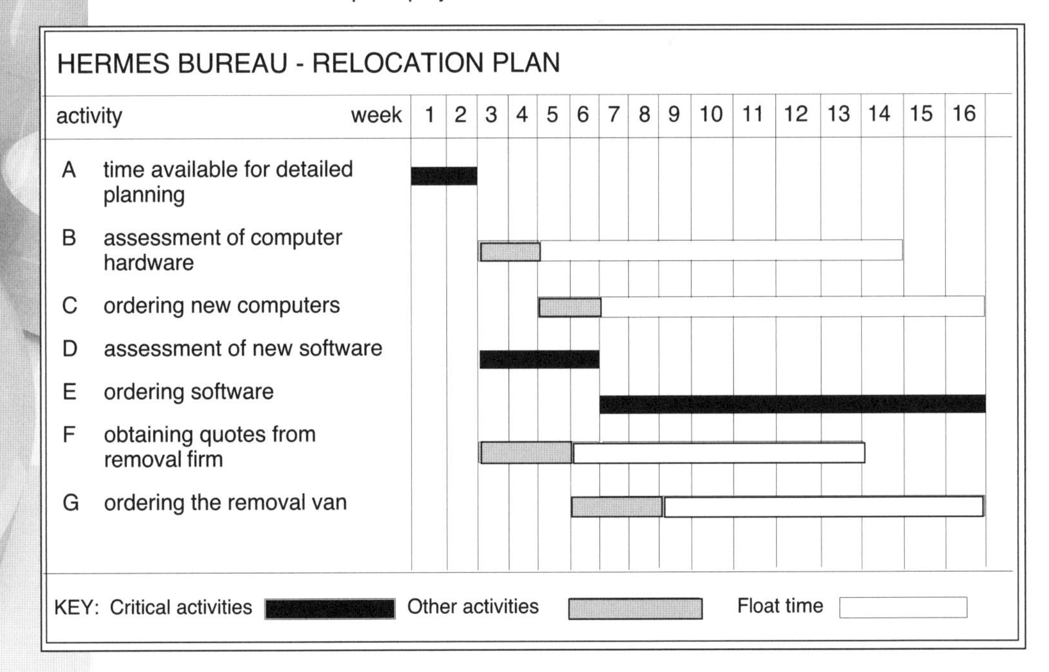

You can also see from this chart that the black bars represent the *priority* activities: planning, software assessment and software ordering. The grey bars are the non-priority activities which can be slotted in when convenient. What you effectively have in this chart is the type of prioritised list seen earlier in this chapter, but a prioritised list set on a time schedule. The visual aspect of the chart makes it easier to understand.

action plans

After a series of activities has been scheduled over time, as in the last Case Study, the organisation can then carry out more detailed planning in the form of an **action plan** which will:

- define each activity in detail
- establish start dates for individual activities
- establish target finish dates
- state who is responsible for carrying out each activity
- in some cases state the cost of each activity

This form of plan is a form of checklist which can be regularly monitored and amended as required. Plans rarely go according 'to plan'. Computer spreadsheets are often used for setting out action plans because they can be easily amended and printed out in revised form.

The example below shows an action plan used in a marketing department which is launching a new product. As the months pass, the plan will be monitored, updated and actual costs checked to see if they are within the budget set for the activity .

Enigma Limited

marketing action plan

Product 247G - launch date April

Month	Activity	Person in charge	completed	budget £	actual £
Feb	Book press adverts - trade magazines	RP	6 Feb	5,600	5,750
Feb	Leaflet design	HG	12 Feb	1,200	1,200
Feb	Catalogue design	HG	12 Feb	2,400	2,750
March	Leaflet printing	GF		12,000	
March	Catalogue printing	GF		34,500	
March	Press releases	DD		100	
April	Public launch on 1 April	DD		50,000	
April	Leaflet mailings	DD		5,600	
April	Catalogue mailings	DD		7,500	
April	Mailing of samples	VF		3,500	
May	Telesales to follow mailings	DD		2,400	

MONITORING AND CHANGING PRIORITIES

So far in this chapter we have dealt with the techniques for planning and prioritising tasks. We have also looked at the planning aids that can be used, ranging from simple 'To Do' checklists to complex schedules and action plans for projects.

the importance of monitoring

But things never go quite according to plan. The unexpected can occur and what seems like a quiet productive day can turn into a stressful time, full of awkward decisions. An important aspect of working is therefore **monitoring** what is going on. Is everything going to plan? If it is, tasks can be carried out in the decided order of priority. If it is not, changes will have to be made: tasks may change in order of priority, tasks may have to be delegated or delayed, or you may have to go to a higher authority and ask for help.

This planning and monitoring process is shown in the diagram shown below.

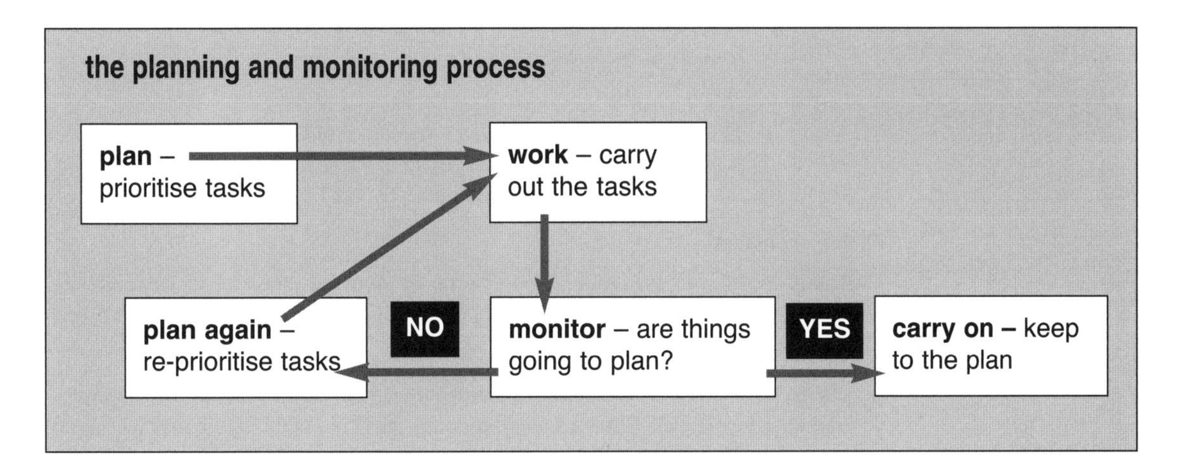

dealing with changed priorities

At the beginning of a working day you are likely to have a set list of tasks and priorities. You may have a 'To Do' list to work from and a diary for specific timed events. But all sorts of things can happen, hopefully not at the same time:

- your colleague, who shares your work, is off sick, so you have twice as much paperwork to deal with as usual
- the post – which brings the bulk of the documents you have to process – does not arrive because of a postal strike
- your email system breaks down because there is a virus in the server

These situations call for tasks to be re-prioritised, for resources to be assessed, and for assistance to be called for. Your work plans will have to be changed, as we will see in the Case Study which follows.

Case Study

FLICK'S DAY – CHANGING THE PRIORITIES

Flick works as an accounts assistant at the Liverpool head office of Estro PLC, a company that makes vacuum cleaners.

The Case Study which starts on page 87 showed how Flick prioritised her tasks on one working day – Thursday 6 February.

In this Case Study we will see how she copes with unexpected events on that day by changing the priorities of her tasks and asking for help from managerial staff where appropriate.

To recap on what Flick had planned for Thursday:

1 The urgent tasks were to provide the January sales figures for the Accounts Manager and to help with moving the computers in the afternoon.
2 Flick had planned to get some jars of office coffee at lunchtime.
3 There was the normal daily sales order processing work and filing to be done.
4 Flick also had to provide some customer activity printouts for the following day and had been asked to move some filing records.

Flick's problems

Flick was faced with a number of problems as soon as she got to work on the Thursday. These meant that her carefully thought out work plan was in trouble and would have to be revised. The problems were:

1 **09.30**. Her colleague, Kirsty, who helped her with her sales order processing work had to go home sick. She had eaten a dodgy curry the night before and was in no fit state to work. There was a trainee working on the invoicing as well, but Flick doubted if this trainee could cope with the extra work involved.

2 **10.00**. Flick saw from Kirsty's note that she had to give the Accounts Manager the January sales figures 'as soon as possible'. This seemed a bit vague. Did it mean during the morning, or would later in the day be OK?

3 **11.30**. Flick's printer jammed and a long run of invoices was ruined. She could not seem to get it to work again.

4 **12.00**. The Human Resources Manager phoned through to ask if she could 'pop in' to see her at 1.45. Was she free then? Flick knew that she had to move the computers at 2.00.

5 **12.30**. Flick realised that she was going to have to work for most of her lunch break. What about the coffee she was supposed to be getting?

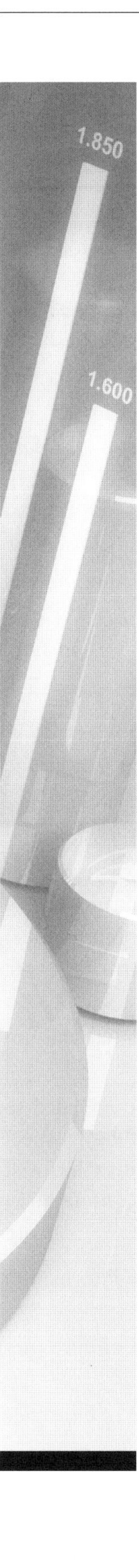

Flick was faced with a number of situations which clearly meant that her work plan was going to be disrupted and would have to be revised. But how was she to do this? She obviously needed to make suggestions to the management about what should be done. Some of the decisions would have to be made by the management.

09.30 Kirsty away off sick

Kirsty's absence would mean that Kirsty's routine processing work would have to be done by someone else – either Flick (who was busy anyway) or the trainee – unless it could be left until the next day. Flick would need to assess how much work there was and then speak to the line manager, Josie. The line manager said to Flick 'Do what you can, concentrating on orders from the important customers. The rest will have to wait. I don't think the trainee can be left on her own yet.' Flick was not too happy about this because she was very busy herself. She would have to put some of her other tasks back in order of priority.

10.00 the figures for the Accounts Manager

Flick realised that this was a priority job. To clarify what 'as soon as possible' really meant, she emailed the Accounts Manager who replied that the figures would be needed by lunchtime that day for a meeting in the afternoon. This job remained top priority.

11.30 printer jam

The printer jam had to be referred to the line manager who called in the maintenance engineer. Flick knew that the invoices would have to be printed that day, so she arranged to print them on another printer through the network. She lost valuable time in sorting out this problem and only got back to work at 11.50, by which time she was getting really stressed.

12.00 Human Resources Manager

Flick realised that the 1.45 appointment with the Human Resources Manager would clash with having to move the computers. The request, however, came from a senior manager and took priority over most other tasks. Flick referred the problem to her line manager who said it would be OK for Flick to go to the appointment. Flick was secretly quite pleased to miss lugging the computers about.

12.30 coffee?

Flick realised that she would have to work through some of her lunch hour, which meant that she would not be able to get the coffee. She explained this to Jack, another colleague, who agreed to get the coffee for her.

17.00 end of the day review . . .

Flick is in good spirits because she has had a productive afternoon. Her work targets for the day have largely been completed, despite the changes of plan. The sales figures have been given to the Accounts Manager and much of the sales processing work has been completed. Flick has had an interview with the Human Resources Manager and even arranged for the coffee to be bought. How has this all been achieved? Flick has successfully reworked her priorities and made the most of her resources – delegating tasks and consulting higher authorities where appropriate.

COMMUNICATION AND CONFIDENTIALITY

communication

The Case Study on the last two pages has shown how important it is for Flick to **communicate** with her managers and colleagues. The process of prioritisation does not just mean placing tasks in order, getting stressed and pressing on with them as quickly as possible and hoping for the best. An effective employee will, like Flick, negotiate politely and persuasively with colleagues and superiors to achieve the best solution.

This communication of problems and priorities by employees to management is important because management will want to see the work flow proceed smoothly and without any unexpected hitches. In the case of Flick, she communicated effectively with management:

- she emailed the Accounts Manager to check urgency of providing figures
- she reported the jammed printer to her line manager who called in a maintenance engineer
- she asked her line manager if she could see the HR manager rather than help with moving the computers

At the end of the day Flick's targets were achieved – including getting the coffee – through her effective communication skills.

confidentiality

As we have already seen in Chapter 2 (page 29) maintaining **confidentiality** should always be kept in mind when working as an individual in an office: employees always have to take care with confidentiality of information held both in paper records and also on computer. For example:

- payroll information should always be kept strictly confidential and not revealed to other employees
- information about customers and suppliers should never be revealed to outsiders – the only exception to this is in the case of banks if they suspect customers of money laundering from drug dealing or funding terrorist activities; here the law requires that the business *must* reveal information to the police authorities

Also, the **Data Protection Act** protects the confidentiality of information about individuals. It applies to:

- personal data held on computer – eg a computer database of customer names, addresses, telephone numbers, sales details
- accessible paper-based records – eg a card index file system of customer details

Chapter Summary

- An individual working independently should be able to combine efficiency and effectiveness in planning the daily workload.
- Employees working independently should develop the skill of prioritising tasks and be able to plan their activities accordingly.
- A 'rule of thumb' order of priority for tasks is:
  1 urgent and important tasks
  2 urgent and less important tasks
  3 important and not urgent tasks
  4 tasks that are neither urgent nor important
- Employees should be familiar with different types of planning aids. They should be able to write their own 'To Do' lists and diaries. They should be able to understand planning aids such as project planning schedules and action plans, but they will not have to draw them up.
- Employees should understand the need to monitor the progress of a work plan over time in order to meet deadlines, and have the flexibility to be able to re-prioritise if unexpected events happen.
- Employees should be able to communicate with management if they need help; they should also be able to delegate tasks if the need arises, maintaining confidentiality where appropriate.

Key Terms

effective — getting the result that you want

efficient — a task done with the minimum of wastage of effort and resources

non-routine task — an unexpected task which is not part of the everyday work of an employee

urgent task — a task which has a pressing deadline

important task — a task which an employee needs to complete and which significantly affects other employees

'To Do' list — a checklist of tasks, made by an individual, which can be ticked off when they are completed

schedule — a chart used for planning projects which organises tasks in terms of time and priority

action plan — a checklist for a series of activities, listing the main tasks, when they have to be done and by whom

monitoring — the process of examining the progress of the work plan and re-prioritising tasks where appropriate

Activities

5.1 What is the difference between a routine task and a non-routine task? Give examples of both from your own experience of the workplace. (If you have not been at work, ask family and friends.)

5.2 Explain what is meant by the term 'prioritisation of tasks' and state the two main factors that are involved in the decision making process.

5.3 (a) Define the difference between an urgent task and an important task.

(b) Normally an urgent task should be done before an important task. Give an example of a situation where the opposite may be true.

5.4 Give two examples of planning aids which are used by most employees in the workplace.

5.5 The eleven tasks below are examples of activities which a payroll assistant may have to carry out in an Accounts Department of a medium-sized company. It is Monday in the last week of the month and the office has just opened. Employees in the organisation are paid monthly, on the last day of the month, which is at the end of this week. The payroll has to be run through the computer on Monday and BACS instructions sent to the bank on Tuesday so that employees can be paid on Friday.

You are to reorganise the list, placing the tasks in order of priority.

- Look at the section diary and compare with your 'To Do' list.
- Send email to Marketing Department asking for monthly overtime figures to be sent through - they should have been received last Friday.
- Check that details of hours worked (including overtime) have been received from all departments.
- Distribute the departmental post.
- Draw up a notice advertising a staff trip out for next month.
- Process the hours of all the employees on the computer. Print out pay details and a payroll summary, including the schedule setting out the amount which will have to be paid to HM Revenue & Customs for income tax and National Insurance Contributions by 19th of the next month.
- Pass the payroll printouts to your line manager for checking, and when approved, print out the payslips for distribution.
- Put a note in the diary for the HM Revenue & Customs payment to be prepared on 5th of next month.
- Print out payroll statistics from the computer for your line manager - they are required for next week.
- Prepare the BACS payroll schedule for the bank to process on Tuesday.
- Pass the BACS payroll schedule to your line manager for checking.

5.6 *Note: this Activity can only be carried out after you have completed Activity 5.5.*

When you have prioritised your tasks in the payroll section, a number of events happen during the day which mean you might not be able to do all the work you had planned.

How would you react to the following situations? In each case explain what you would do and what the implications would be for your work plan for the day.

Remember that you can ask for help from colleagues or refer difficulties to a higher authority.

(a) You get a call from Reception at 9.30, saying that your car in the car park has still got its lights on.

(b) At 10.30 the Human Resources Manager calls to ask if you would like to sit in on a Quality Circle meeting at 14.00 to discuss Customer Service.

(c) You get a call from reception at 11.30 saying that a friend has called and wants to talk on a personal matter.

(d) When you are processing the email from Admin Department giving overtime hours, you notice that two employees are recorded as having worked 50 hours overtime. The normal maximum is 5 hours.

(e) The computer system crashes, just as you are finishing processing the payroll.

6 Working as a member of a team

this chapter covers...

This chapter explains the need for a person working in an organisation to be able to work as a member of a team in order to help to achieve the objectives of that organisation.

Team members must be able to:

- *identify what they have to do in practical terms to contribute to the work of the team*
- *keep to a plan*
- *keep to deadlines that have been set*
- *appreciate the consequences of not completing tasks that they have been set*
- *appreciate the consequences to the team of not completing tasks within the deadlines that have been set*

Team members must also be able to know what to do when conflicts arise between team members. They must be able to:

- *identify situations where conflicts can arise within a team*
- *understand the consequences of conflict within a team on the achievement of the team's objectives*
- *suggest ways of sorting out and resolving conflicts*
- *identify situations where conflicts will need to be referred to a higher authority for sorting out*

TEAMWORK

what is a team?

Working with others implies the need for teamwork. It is easy to start to define a team by giving examples – a football team, a workplace team – and explaining that they work together – sometimes well and sometimes not quite so well. In the case of a football team this means that they sometimes lose.

But what exactly is a team?

A team is a group of people working together to achieve defined objectives.

In the case of a football team, the objective is clearly to play skillfully and defeat the other side. In the workplace a team can be a 'section group' working in one part of an office – eg a payroll section – or it can be a group working on a project, eg a group set up to improve customer service. The objective of a 'section group' will be to complete the work set efficiently, to a high standard and within the normal deadlines. The goal of a 'project group' will be to achieve the overall objective, eg an assessment of customer service and an overall improvement in standards.

the benefits of teamwork

People working in a team often achieve better results than if they work on their own. The benefits include:

- **pooling of skills and abilities:** some people are better at some tasks and some are better at others, and so a team will take advantage of individual strengths and overcome individual weaknesses
- **creative thinking**: working with other people means that individuals can be stimulated to create and share ideas on a scale that would probably not be possible if they were working on their own
- **motivation**: people get a 'buzz' out of working in a team – it gets people going and brings its rewards when the team is successful
- **help and support**: team members usually support each other when support is needed – this can take the form of advice, moral support and assisting with or taking over tasks which may be causing a problem

problems with teamwork

It should be pointed out, however, that teamwork is not always the simple answer to achieving objectives. Team members can sometimes be unco-operative and disruptive. When this happens, the other team members – and particularly the team leader – will have to sort out the situation, and if they are unable to do so, the problem will have to be referred to a higher authority. Problems with teamwork are covered later in this chapter (pages 100 to 104).

working at teamwork

Teamwork requires that team members are dedicated to achieving the team objective. This means that team members should:

- be committed to the work of the team
- understand their role in the team and the tasks they are allotted
- take full responsibility for what they do
- assume joint responsibility for the work of the whole team
- take note of and work to the schedules imposed by the team

communication and teamwork

The vital link between team members is **communication**. Although employees will communicate with outsiders – customers and suppliers, for example – it is the effectiveness of the internal communication channels which will make a significant difference to the success of teamwork. Communication channels include:

- oral communication – talking to people face-to-face
- oral communication – talking to people on the telephone
- written communication – notes, letters, memoranda, reports
- electronic communication – email

Methods of communication have been described in Chapter 4.

communication at work

the importance of face-to-face communication

no need to worry about facial expressions on the telephone!

CREATING AN EFFECTIVE TEAM

what does a team need?

A workplace team can be a group – a section – which works together on a daily basis, or it can be a special project team set up for a specific and limited purpose. A team needs to establish for itself:

- **objectives** – eg a level of quality in the case of a 'section' team, a specific result in the case of a project team
- levels of **resources** – people, equipment, time, money
- a definition of **working methods** – deciding how the work is to be carried out, and by whom
- **schedules** – time targets for specific tasks

In the case of a work 'section' team these factors will be based on current practice, and will be refined over time, improved perhaps by regular team meetings to discuss the way the team works.

In the case of a 'project' team, the team members will sit down and plan out all these factors at the start of the project.

types of team member

If you have worked in any form of team, you will know that there are many different types of character that can make up that team:

- the leader – who may be a natural leader, appointed by the group, or who may be an employee appointed to a position of responsibility
- an ideas person who provides inspiration to the group
- the steady worker who gets things done
- the slacker and complainer who does not get things done and causes problems
- the person who provides moral and practical support to others when problems arise

ideal qualities of a team member

In order to create good working relationships, as a team member you should ideally:

- be pleasant and polite to other team members
- be prepared to co-operate, even if you do not agree with everything that is decided
- respect the opinions of others and be prepared to listen to what others have to say

- ask others if you need help and be prepared to help others if they need it
- avoid backbiting and criticising the leader behind his/her back
- keep confidences – if information is not to be released, you should keep quiet about it (this is also a requirement of the Data Protection Act)

This probably sounds all very theoretical and ideal. In the Case Study on page 102 we examine how this works in practice. First, however, we must also explain what can go wrong in working relationships, and how those problems can be resolved.

DEALING WITH PROBLEMATIC WORKING RELATIONSHIPS

what can go wrong?

Problems are often caused by disagreements. These disagreements can either be resolved within the team, or exceptionally they may have to be referred to a higher authority. There are two main causes of disagreement:

- **the nature of the work** itself and the way it is carried out – for example a new line manager joining the team with very different ideas about how the work should be tackled
- **personal conflicts** within the group – clashes of personality types, even extending to bullying and other forms of harassment

Very often the two areas combine to produce a problem which can be very difficult to sort out. Look at the illustration below which shows what can irritate other people at work and cause problems in working relationships.

causes of breakdowns in working relationships

I do not like people who are . . .
- inefficient
- inflexible
- rude
- over-critical
- over-sensitive
- sexist

I do not like people who have . . .
- an inflated opinion of themselves
- personal hygiene problems

sorting out disagreements within a team

It is important for team members to resolve problems in working relationships themselves, within the team itself, if that is possible.

If the problem is simply one which relates to **the work itself** – for example procedures for the processing of sales orders – it could be sorted out by informal discussion between team members (ie work colleagues) and then referral to a higher authority.

If the problem is one which relates to a **personal conflict between team members** – for example 'she's too slow at her work, and always texting her boyfriend' or 'he's a real pain to work with because he's always making insulting remarks' – the problem should be sorted by other means, for example:

- observing other people dealing with that person – do they have the same problems?
- talking it over with other members of the team – do they think the same way, or is it just you getting things out of proportion?
- talking to the person involved – do they actually realise how they affect other people?

If there really is a problem – and it's not just you being negative or over-sensitive – then the matter should be raised with a higher authority.

taking the matter further – grievance procedures

If the working relationship problem is actually one of harassment – for example bullying or someone making passes at you – the matter should definitely be raised with a higher authority. If it is the line manager who is the cause of the problem, the matter should be referred to a more senior authority.

If the matter is very serious, the **grievance procedure** can be adopted. A **grievance** is a complaint against the employer. Grievances can include:

- unfair treatment by managers – for example, being passed over for promotion because of gender or race; unfair dismissal (an extreme case!)
- unfair pay – men paid more than women for the same work

All employers must have a written grievance procedure. This will be set down in writing and made available to all employees. It will state:

- the person to whom the employee must go with their complaint – often a chat with the employee's line manager (as we saw above) will be enough to sort matters out
- if the employee is still not happy with the way they are being treated they will be allowed to make a formal complaint to a more senior manager

We will now look at a Case Study which shows how working relationships are developed within a work team, and the way in which problems can be resolved.

Case Study

WORKING ON RELATIONSHIPS

situation

The accounts staff of Hermes Limited, which sells motor accessories, have been asked to provide sales information for the Marketing Department. The team from the Accounts Department is headed up by Jen, a line manager. She will be helped by two accounts assistants, Tom and Jacqui.

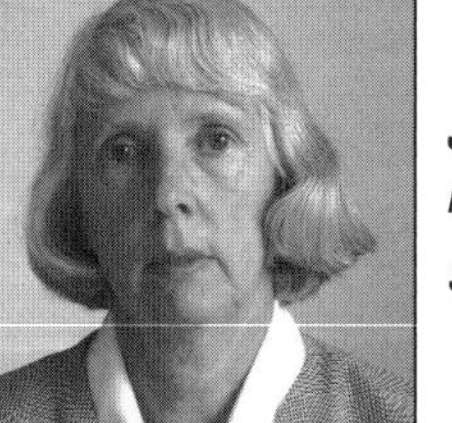

Jen *is a line manager, an organiser, experienced at her work and respected by staff.*

She has worked for the company for twenty years.

Tom *is a mature and experienced accounts assistant, a hard worker, accurate and with an eye for detail. He is not as fast as some assistants, but he can be relied upon to keep to deadlines.*

He is also ready to help others when they need assistance. He has a quiet personality, and is popular in the office.

He has worked under Jen for three years, but she has during this time criticised him for being too slow at his work.

Jacqui *is a confident accounts assistant, always ready to give her opinion on how to get things done.*

She is sometimes inaccurate because she tends to work too quickly.

She is capable of achieving her targets, however, when given help and encouragement.

the project

The Accounts Department has been asked by the Marketing Department to provide regular monthly statistics relating to customer sales. This will require

- analysis of sales figures extracted from the computer accounting system
- the setting up of spreadsheets to analyse the data
- the setting up of a monthly report template on a word-processing program

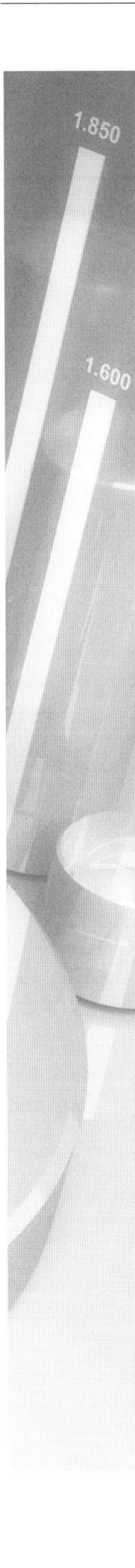

the meeting

Jen calls a meeting of her team to discuss how they are going to set up this system and maintain it to produce the monthly statistics.

They decide the following:

objective — the objective is to provide regular monthly sales statistics for the Marketing Department

resources — two assistants (Tom and Jacqui), computers and computer time, data held on the computer

work scheduling
- Tom, who has good IT skills, is to work on the spreadsheets and the report format. He will then help Jacqui input the data into the spreadsheets and extract the report
- Jacqui is to extract the data held on the computer accounting system

deadlines
- 2 weeks for Tom to complete spreadsheets and Jacqui to extract the data
- 2 further weeks for transferring data to the spreadsheets and producing the first report
- total time allowed 4 weeks

what actually happened

Week 1

At the end of the first week Jen calls a meeting to monitor progress on the project. Tom has worked to schedule and has prepared the spreadsheets set up to process the statistics. Jacqui has fallen behind in extracting the data, which means that Tom has insufficient test data to input. Jen says, laughing 'Don't worry, Jacqui will soon catch up, she is a good quick worker.'

Week 2

During week 2 Tom finds out that Jacqui's data is incomplete and inaccurate. He offers to put it right for her, so that he can ensure that the data for the spreadsheets will be accurate. Jacqui is happy to accept Tom's assistance.

Tom also completes the word-processed report template. He knows that the deadline is important, because if the project falls behind, the Marketing Department will not get their figures on time.

At the end of the second week Jen calls a meeting to monitor progress. She is pleased with the progress made and praises Jacqui for her good work.

Weeks 3 and 4

During the final two weeks, Tom and Jacqui are scheduled to work together to complete the project, and it is during these two weeks that major problems occur.

Tom resents the fact that he has to help Jacqui to meet the deadlines, but what really annoys him is that Jen does not recognise his effort.

Tom has two problematic working relationships – and neither of them are really his fault.

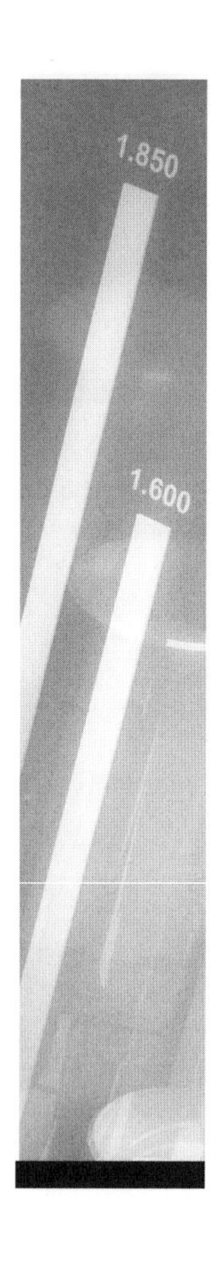

So what are Tom's practical alternatives?

1 Tom can refuse to help Jacqui.
2 Tom can complain to Jen about Jacqui's inaccuracy.
3 Tom can carry on and do more than his fair share of the work.

the solution

Tom decides to chat to his mate Dave about these problems.

the Jacqui problem

Dave suggests that Tom talks to other colleagues to see how they deal with Jacqui, but in the end he thinks Tom will have to accept the Jacqui situation as there will always be people at work who work less hard than their colleagues.

Tom is unlikely to get any backing from Jen who is under the impression that Jacqui is a fast and accurate worker and he is slow.

If Tom refuses to help Jacqui, he will be seen as being unco-operative and not helping the development of good working relations. Tom has little choice here but to carry on.

the Jen problem

Dave suggests that Tom takes the initiative and talks to Jen herself about the situation. This may not be the most obvious solution, but it does seem that Jen does not realise that Jacqui is unreliable. A frank and reasoned discussion with Jen may help to change her attitude.

If all this fails Tom should make an appointment to talk to his departmental manager or to a Human Resources manager.

In the meantime he has his deadlines to meet and the project to complete . . .

Chapter Summary

- Effective teamwork is needed if a group of employees is to achieve its objectives.
- The benefits of teamwork include: the pooling of skills and abilities, the opportunity for creative thinking, motivation within the team, help and support from team members.
- Teams can be normal day-to-day working groups, or they can be special project teams set up for specific purposes.
- Working relationships within a team can go wrong, either because of the work itself, or because of a breakdown in the relationship – or both.
- When working relationships within a team do go wrong, they should ideally be resolved within the group. If that is not possible, they may have to be resolved by a higher authority using the grievance procedure.

team — a group of people working together to achieve defined objectives

grievance procedure — the formal procedure to follow when you have a complaint against your employer

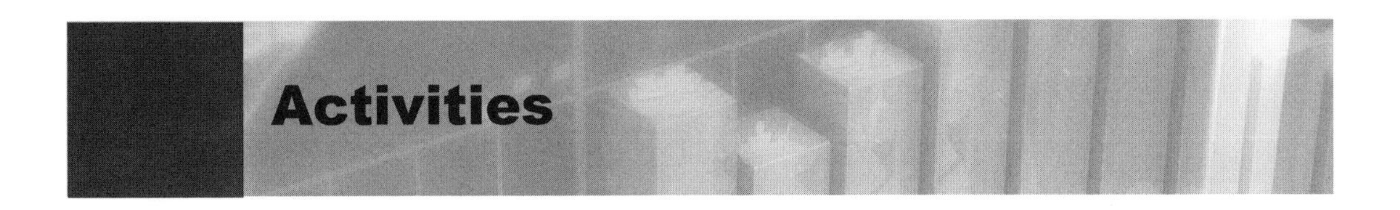

Activities

6.1 Explain the meaning of the term 'team' and outline the benefits of working in a team.

6.2 State the objectives of the team in which you work (or a team in which a friend or family member works).

6.3 Write down the six qualities a team member should ideally possess to enable the team to function effectively.

Optional task: give yourself a score out of ten for each quality, add up the total score and convert to a percentage. How do you think you have done? How do you compare with your colleagues? How could you improve your teamwork skills?

6.4 A new colleague, Jake, has just joined your team, and you find him to be an absolute pain – he thinks he knows everything, and doesn't. He also talks about colleagues and the line manager behind their backs.

What action could you take to deal with a character like Jake?

6.5 Jasmina, a friend of yours, has worked in a payroll section for a number of years. She has a poor working relationship with her line manager, Tim, and as a result has been passed over for promotion a number of times. The line manager has been heard to say 'There's no point in promoting her and giving her all the extra training, she wants to have a baby, and may well leave the firm when it suits her.'

What practical advice can you give Jasmina about dealing with her working relationship with the line manager?

7 CPD – developing skills and knowledge at work

this chapter covers...

This chapter explains the need for an individual working in an organisation to acquire knowledge and develop a variety of skills in order to

- *improve himself or herself*
- *meet the needs of the organisation*

A common way to achieve this is by undertaking a programme of Continuing Professional Development (CPD).

- *This process, which should be formally recorded by the employee, might involve:*
  - *in-house training courses and technical updates*
  - *external training courses*
  - *researching the area of work on the internet and in publications*
- *Employees should be able to identify their development needs and objectives for achievement, involving their line manager in the process.*
- *These objectives should be SMART, ie* ***S****pecific,* ***M****easurable,* ***A****chievable,* ***R****ealistic and* ***T****imely.*
- *The employee should monitor and review his or her progress against these objectives on a regular basis.*
- *The development of employee skills and knowledge helps to improve the efficiency of the organisation and will benefit all concerned.*

CONTINUING PROFESSIONAL DEVELOPMENT (CPD)

what is CPD?

Continuing Professional Development (CPD) can be defined as:

the learning activities undertaken by employees to maintain, improve and broaden the knowledge and skills required in their professional lives

Continuing Professional Development (CPD) is an ongoing cycle – a process involving both employee and employer. It is normally up to the employee to complete the planned activities in order to achieve the level of professional competence required by the professional body to which he or she belongs. Study the diagram below and then read the text that follows.

start here

CPD – achieving your development needs

what are my development needs now?
am I fully trained?
do I know enough about my work?

what are my objectives?
what training do I need?
what knowledge do I need?
what qualifications could I take?

how can I achieve my objectives?
in-house training courses?
in-house technical updates?
coaching from colleagues?
external training courses?
taking a qualification?
reading books and journals?
accessing websites?
using IT training, eg CD-ROMs?

how well have I achieved?
have my objectives been achieved?
am I happy with my progress?
is my employer happy with my progress?

In order to improve your **performance** and career prospects – your **development needs** – you need to take stock of your current position and identify exactly where it is you want to go. The diagram above shows a process which involves four stages:

1 what are my development needs now?
2 what are my objectives?
3 how can I achieve my objectives?
4 how well have I achieved them?

The process, of course, is continuous and subject to continual review. We will look at each of the four stages in turn.

WHAT ARE MY DEVELOPMENT NEEDS NOW?

You may be in employment at present, or it is possible that you are not in work. Whatever the situation, you will need to take a look at what your personal development needs are. You need to carry out a form of personal 'audit' of your **knowledge** (what you know) and **skills** (how you put it into practice). How do you do this? You need to ask yourself a number of questions and also talk them over with colleagues.

You will see that a number of the following questions can apply to people who are not in work:

1. Am I content with what I am doing at present?
2. Am I confident that I have the background knowledge for what I am doing at work?
3. Am I up-to-date with changes in the knowledge and skills required for the area in which I work ?
4. Do I need further training for what I am doing at work?
5. Do my skills need developing? For example, do I need to go on a spreadsheet course? Do I need to improve my computer skills?

talk it over with your manager

6. Where do I see myself working in a year's time?

If you are at work you may well discuss these issues on a regular basis with your manager as part of the **appraisal** process. At the interview, objectives should be set, training needs identified and promotion prospects explored.

You should always be given the opportunity of discussing with your manager the ways in which you can develop your **skills** and **knowledge** and improve your performance.

WHAT ARE MY OBJECTIVES?

When you have thought about your development and career needs, and discussed them with others, you will be in a position to set specific objectives – targets – for achievement. These will not be vague and woolly like 'I want to be a manager' or 'I want to be better at my work' but will be very specific. For example you might say that within the next twelve months . . . .

> *'I need to learn more about spreadsheets because they are used a lot in the Accounts Department.'*

'I need to learn more about the Sage computer accounting system. I can do the basics, but haven't a clue about doing journal entries. I don't really know my debits from my credits!'

'I'd like to do an accounting qualification – it should help me to get on in my career.'

'I need to know more about the theoretical background to the accounting work I am doing at the moment.'

These objectives may be met through a variety of activities, for example:

- **on-the-job training** – being coached by another employee, attending formal in-house courses, following 'tutorials' provided online or with software used in the office (eg CD-ROMs)
- **technical updates** carried out in-house – for example, using updated payroll software at the beginning of a new tax year, or when a new software version is released, and making use of the technical telephone 'helpline' offered by the software company (eg by Sage)
- **external training courses** run by your organisation (if it has a separate training centre) or by an independent training body – for example a Health & Safety course or Excel spreadsheet course run by the local Chamber of Commerce or College
- **research** on the internet or through reading publications related to the tasks you do at work – for example, if you work in an Accounts Department you may need to get up-to-date with the ever-increasing internal security measures needed for handling debit and credit card transactions
- taking **qualifications** such as a Level 2 qualification in Accounting and Finance – studying at a local college or with a distance learning provider

The important point here is that you cannot expect to do everything at once. You should have the opportunity to sit down with your manager and work out a suitable and realistic programme which can be followed and then reviewed after a set period of time.

objectives that are SMART

When setting objectives you should always aim for **SMART** objectives. SMART is a widely used acronym which, when used in CPD, helps to ensure that the objectives set are suitable and effective for the person concerned. In practice, the words represented by these letters do vary to a certain extent, but a common example requires that the objectives should be:

Specific

Measurable

Achievable

Realistic

Timely

In other words, each of the CPD objectives agreed with the employee's manager should be:

- **Specific** – they should be clear and well-defined so that the employee knows what is expected of them and the manager can monitor and assess how successful the employee is at achieving the objective.
- **Measurable** – the employee and the manager should be able to tell how well the objective is being achieved. For example if the employee is taking an external course or qualification, there will be grades and exam success rates to provide a measure of success.
- **Achievable** – the objective must be within the competence of the employee. All resources needed by the employee must be made available by the management (eg equipment, time, access to people, funding for an external course).
- **Realistic** – this relates in a way to 'achievable' and asks whether the employee is able and willing to work to achieve the target set. In short, does the employee have the necessary 'belief'?
- **Timely** – a timescale must be set for the objective. Can the objective be achieved within the time target?

HOW CAN I ACHIEVE MY OBJECTIVES?

The SMART objectives the employee plans to achieve by definition need to be made very specific. For example:

'I need to go on an advanced Excel spreadsheet course at the local Chamber of Commerce Training Centre so that I can process the Sales data and produce charts for my manager.'

'I need to work alongside Kulvinder for a week so that I can learn more about operating our Sage computer accounting system.'

'I want to enrol on a Level 2 course in accounting at the local college because I want to be promoted within the department.'

> *'I need to read that Osborne Books accounting textbook recommended by my colleague because it will give me the background knowledge I need.'*

You may already have identified the fact that what this person really needs to do is to enrol on an accounting course with a training provider, such as a local college. This will provide the theoretical and practical background to a career in an accounts office and also help with promotion prospects, as will be seen in the Case Study at the bottom of this page.

HOW WELL HAVE I ACHIEVED?

The process of personal planning never stands still. As in any planning process, achievement will have to be monitored on a regular basis, eg every twelve months at the annual appraisal interview when both the employer and the employee will need to re-assess the situation. The planning process can then start all over again – new objectives, new targets, a new action plan.

In the Case Study which follows we look at the personal planning carried out by a typical accounting employee.

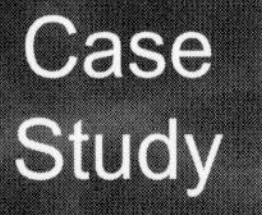

CPD – MAKING THE MOST OF YOUR RESOURCES

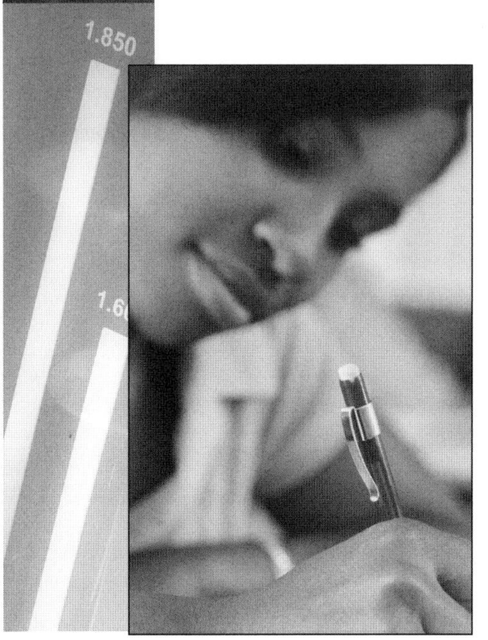

situation

Kelly works in the Accounts Department of CompLink Limited, a computer supplies wholesaler. She moves to some extent between the sections, but spends most of her time in Sales Ledger, where she processes orders on the computer accounting system, checks documentation and has started basic work in Credit Control, sending out statements.

Kelly wants to get on in her job and career. At her appraisal interview in July, she agreed with her manager that she should achieve certain targets within the next twelve months as part of her Continuing Professional Development.

These objectives included:

- in-house training in credit control procedures in the Accounts Department, achieved by work-shadowing (working alongside a senior colleague in Credit Control)
- attending an intensive two day training course in computer accounting at a local external training provider

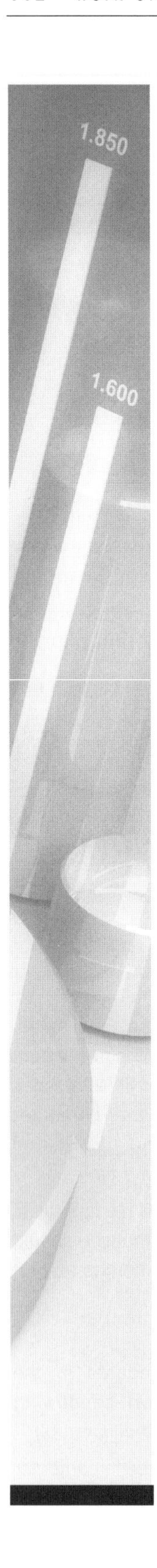

- enrolment at the local college to take a Level 2 Accounting course, which runs from September to the following June when she will have to sit her exams

solution

Kelly makes good use of the various resources chosen to help her in her CPD:

colleagues

Kelly can talk to her colleagues and make the most of their experience and knowledge, picking up tips about dealing with procedures and situations. This is particularly useful in Credit Control where Kelly can learn how to deal with slow payers - interpreting all their lame excuses about not paying (eg 'the cheque has been signed, but we haven't sent it yet' or 'we don't seem to have received the invoice'). She will also learn how to send out the appropriate chaser letters without offending the 'important' customers who invariably pay late.

training provider

Studying accounting is never an easy option, but Kelly finds that having a good teacher and a lively class helps her understand the more difficult areas of the course. She is able to ask questions about the areas she finds difficult and is given help when her trial balance doesn't balance.

textbooks

Kelly uses the Osborne Books range of accounting texts and finds that they help her understand difficult concepts and prepare well for her assessments. She is online at home and finds the Student resources on the publisher's website (www.osbornebooks.co.uk) a big help.

other websites

The websites of accounting bodies such as AAT are full of useful information and links. The site www.aat.org.uk provides Student Forums and offers e-learning opportunities.

Kelly also uses the website of HM Revenue & Customs (www.HMRC.gov.uk) to answer queries about VAT which have cropped up at work.

and finally . . .

At the end of the twelve months Kelly will discuss with her manager the extent to which she has been successful in achieving her objectives:

- Following her in-house training and work-shadowing, is she now able to operate the customer debt chasing system without supervision?
- Did she complete her computer accounting course successfully and has she been able to take on more advanced input work?
- Did she pass her June accounting exams?

She will then be in a position to set the objectives for the following twelve months. For example she may have further in-house training, go on a computer spreadsheet course, and take the next stage of her accounting qualification.

RECORDING CPD

It is important to record CPD as an ongoing process so that the employee and employer can monitor and review its success or shortcomings, and take appropriate action as necessary. There is no set format for a CPD record, but a typical form will include sections to cover the overall **goal** of CPD as discussed with the manager, and the specific objectives – **learning needs –** which will enable the goal to be achieved.

The record should be kept up-to-date and form the basis of a regular (eg six-monthly) discussion between employer and employee. The extract from a completed CPD form shown below includes:

- a box for the **CPD goal** of the employee – this is for a general statement
- a section for a **Learning need** subdivided into four linked areas:
  1. **Assess** box – what do you need to learn?
  2. **Plan** box – what are the activities involved and the target date?
  3. **Action** box – what have you learned?
  4. **Evaluate** – how far have you got, do you need to do more?

  There are likely to be a number of 'Learning need' boxes to complete.

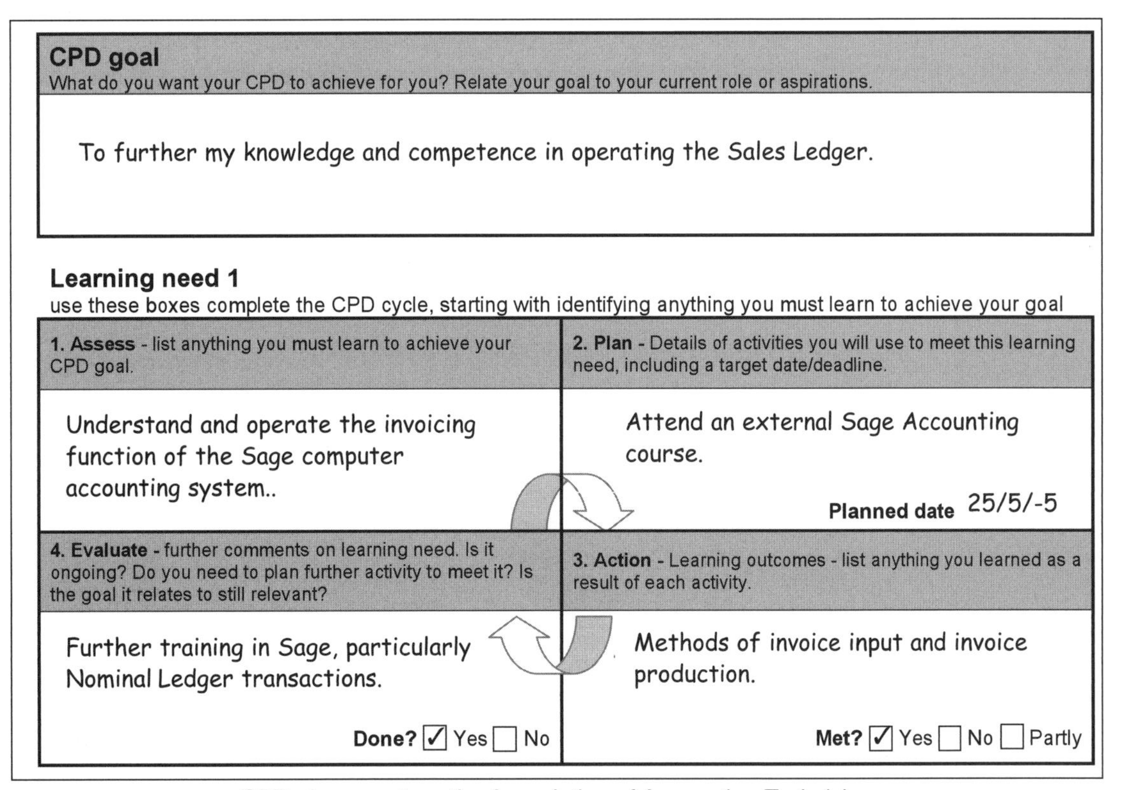
CPD goal
What do you want your CPD to achieve for you? Relate your goal to your current role or aspirations.

To further my knowledge and competence in operating the Sales Ledger.

Learning need 1
use these boxes complete the CPD cycle, starting with identifying anything you must learn to achieve your goal

1. Assess - list anything you must learn to achieve your CPD goal.

Understand and operate the invoicing function of the Sage computer accounting system..

2. Plan - Details of activities you will use to meet this learning need, including a target date/deadline.

Attend an external Sage Accounting course.

Planned date 25/5/-5

3. Action - Learning outcomes - list anything you learned as a result of each activity.

Methods of invoice input and invoice production.

Met? ☑ Yes ☐ No ☐ Partly

4. Evaluate - further comments on learning need. Is it ongoing? Do you need to plan further activity to meet it? Is the goal it relates to still relevant?

Further training in Sage, particularly Nominal Ledger transactions.

Done? ☑ Yes ☐ No

CPD plan, courtesy the Association of Accounting Technicians

Chapter Summary

- Improving your own performance through Continuing Professional Development (CPD) involves a number of stages, starting with you assessing what you do at work (if you are in work) and thinking about where you want your career to take you.
- You should then set defined objectives (targets). If you are at work this is normally done with your employer – very often in an appraisal interview.
- These objectives should be 'SMART':

  Specific

  Measurable

  Achievable

  Realistic

  Timely
- You should then work out how you are going to achieve these objectives, assessing the resources you are going to need. The extent of these will depend whether or not you are at work: you may consider tapping into the expertise of your colleagues, training in-house and externally, taking a qualification, obtaining study material in various media.
- The final stage in the personal development process is to review and evaluate your progress and to establish new targets and action plans. If you are at work, this may be carried out with your employer as part of the regular appraisal process.
- All stages in the CPD process should be clearly documented.

Key Terms

CPD — Continuing Professional Development (CPD) involves an agreed set of learning activities undertaken by employees to maintain, improve and broaden the knowledge and skills required in their professional lives

objectives — specific 'SMART' targets for development needs

knowledge — what you need to know to enable you to do a job at work

skills — the ability to put knowledge into practice

appraisal — the process whereby a manager interviews an employee on a regular basis, assessing past performance and identifying development needs

performance — your success rate in achieving your development needs

Activities

7.1 Describe briefly the main stages in the Continuing Professional Development (CPD) process.

7.2 What does 'SMART' stand for and why is it important for the setting of CPD objectives?

7.3 Who are the main people who are involved in CPD discussions and what should they be able to achieve in their discussions during the course of the CPD?

7.4 If you are in employment, draft a brief CPD plan for the next 12 months – ie assess your current position and identify the knowledge and skills you will need to develop your performance and career. List the resources that could be made available to help you achieve your objectives.

If you are not employed, carry out a similar exercise based on what you need to do in order to get a position that would be suitable for you.

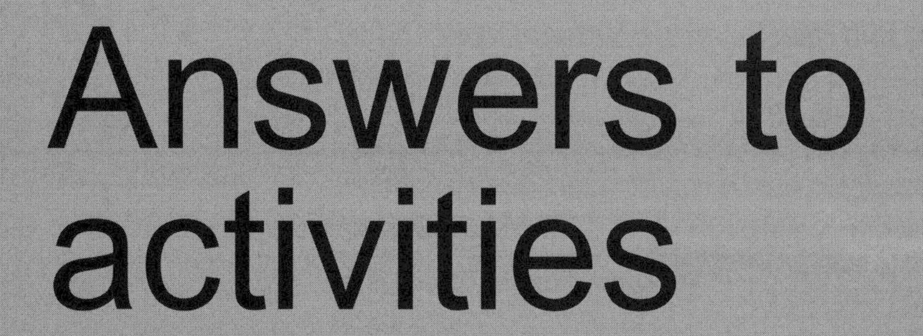

Answers to activities

CHAPTER 1: ACCOUNTING AND FINANCE IN THE WORKPLACE

1.1 (a)

1.2 (b)

1.3 (a)

1.4 (c)

1.5 Internal auditors are employees of the organisation (or people contracted in from outside) to look over its accounting systems; external auditors are independent firms who are contracted by the shareholders of larger companies to validate the accounts.

1.6 (a)
- sales ledger assistant to accounts line manager
- cashier to accounts line manager
- payroll assistant to accounts line manager

(b) the sales ledger assistant

(c) the cashier in the first place, the line manager in the second place

(d) purchases ledger, costing, inventory control

CHAPTER 2: EFFICIENCY AND REGULATION IN THE WORKPLACE

2.1 (b)

2.2 (c)

2.3 (b)

2.4 (d)

2.5 (b)

2.6 (d)

2.7 (a)

CHAPTER 3: WORKING WITH NUMBERS

3.1

(a)

product code	description	quantity	price	unit	total	discount %	net
109BK	Box file (black)	20	4.00	each	80.00	30	56.00
						Total	56.00
						VAT @ 20%	11.20
						TOTAL	67.20

(b)

product code	description	quantity	price	unit	total	discount %	net
235RD	Biros (red)	9	5.60	box of ten	50.40	20	40.32
						Total	40.32
						VAT @ 20%	8.06
						TOTAL	48.38

(c)

product code	description	quantity	price	unit	total	discount %	net
563BL	Year planners (blue)	8	12.95	each	103.60	10	93.24
						Total	93.24
	note that VAT is rounded down to nearest p					VAT @ 20%	18.64
						TOTAL	111.88

3.2 (a) 15% discount on an amount of £45.50 = £6.825, rounded to £6.83

(b) 20% discount on an amount of £44.99 = £8.998, rounded to £9.00

(c) 30% discount on an amount of £21.75 = £6.525, rounded to £6.53

(d) 15% discount on an amount of £390.95 = £58.6425, rounded to £58.64

(e) 30% discount on an amount of £964.55 = £289.365, rounded to £289.37

(f) 2.5% discount on an amount of £35.95 = £0.89875, rounded to £0.90

3.3
(a) £41.00 + VAT of £8.20
(b) £244.00 + VAT of £48.80
(c) £1.90 + VAT of £0.38
(d) £364.00 + VAT of £72.80
(e) £88.00 + VAT of £17.60

3.4

HYPNOS ENTERPRISES – Annual Sales				
	Forecast (benchmark) £	**Actual £**	**Difference £**	**Percentage difference £**
Year 1	600,000	642,000	+ 42,000	7%
Year 2	640,000	608,000	– 32,000	5%

HYPNOS ENTERPRISES – Annual Profits				
	Forecast (benchmark) £	**Actual £**	**Difference £**	**Percentage difference £**
Year 1	64,000	67,200	+ 3,200	5%
Year 2	65,000	63,050	– 1,950	3%

Comments could include the fact that both sales and profits were better than expected in Year 1, but worse than forecast in Year 2. Decisions will have to be made by management. It could be mentioned that action is likely to have to be taken to stop the drop in sales and profits. Students should not be expected to go further than this and should appreciate that it is the role of management to take the necessary decisions

3.5 Pie charts are excellent for showing proportions of a whole – and they are widely used for this – but they do not show relative quantities. They are therefore not very helpful in this context as they are clumsy in illustrating year-to-year trends: the eye cannot easily trace changes in sectors.

Also the pie charts do not tell you the actual divisional or total sales figures for the two years, so as a result you do not know if sales have increased or gone down.

3.6
- mean £9.33
- median £7.90
- mode £11.00

The mean is the most arithmetically reliable as it takes all values into consideration.

CHAPTER 4: COMMUNICATION AT WORK

4.1 (d)

4.2

1 Internal note required here. Short, simple, to the point. The text should mention your name, the date and time of the call, the name of the person to call and the time to call, the telephone number, the nature of the query and credit note number (Neeta will need the document to hand).

2 Fax required here for invoice. The fastest and most efficient form of communication, providing all the information needed. A fax header addressed to James Greenap will need to be completed. Details will be fax number (on file), date and short message stating invoice 29082 is being faxed

An alternative form of communication (not given as an option) would be to scan the invoice and to attach it to an email with suitable text.

3 As this communication is paper-based (the menu) a memo to the staff should be sent round with the menu. This is the fastest and most efficient form of communication. The memo should state the date of the meal and ask for the names of people who want to go and their menu choice. It is important to mention the closing date.

4 As this complaint was received by email it is appropriate to reply using this format. It is fast and effective. The language used should be apologetic and positive (but not over the top). It would be helpful to let the customer know the amount of the credit note due (but not the actual calculation). The goods amount is £200, so the discount will be an extra 10% (ie 30% – 20%) = £20. The amount of the credit note is therefore £20 plus VAT at the appropriate rate (£4.00 @ 20%, at the time of writing).

5 This requires a voicemail message being left. The message should state the name of the caller, the time of the message and the return phone number. The confusion over the product code should be mentioned politely and clarification requested – ie which shirts do they want? It would be helpful if they could confirm this in writing so that a copy could be attached to the purchase order - email would be the fastest and most efficient method.

4.3 (a) The date is missing and the complimentary close should be 'yours faithfully' as there is no name.

(b) The address is missing and the complimentary close should be 'yours sincerely' as there is a name.

CHAPTER 5: WORKING INDEPENDENTLY IN AN ORGANISATION

5.1 A routine task is a task which is part of the everyday activity of the workplace. A non-routine task is an unexpected task. Examples should be given as appropriate.

5.2 Prioritisation of tasks is deciding on the order in which the tasks should be completed. This will depend on the importance and the urgency of the individual tasks.

5.3 (a) An urgent task is a task which is required to be done by a specific deadline; an important task is a task for the completion of which an employee is given personal responsibility and which significantly affects other people.

(b) The situation where the urgent task is relatively unimportant.

5.4 'To Do' list, diary.

5.5 A suggested order for the list:

1 Distribute the departmental post.

2 Look at the section diary and compare with your 'To Do' list.

3 Check that details of hours worked (including overtime) have been received from all departments.

4 Send email to Marketing Department asking for monthly overtime figures to be sent through – they should have been received last Friday.

5 Process the hours of all the employees on the computer. Print out pay details and a payroll summary, including the schedule setting out the amount which will have to be paid to the Inland Revenue for income tax and National Insurance Contributions by 19th of the next month.

6 Pass the payroll printouts to your line manager for checking, and when approved, print out the payslips for distribution.

7 Prepare the BACS payroll schedule for the bank to process on Tuesday.

8 Pass the BACS payroll schedule to your line manager for checking.

9 Put a note in the diary for the Inland Revenue cheque to be prepared on 5th of next month.

10 Print out payroll statistics from the computer for your line manager – they are required for next week.

11 Draw up a notice advertising a staff trip out for next month.

5.6 (a) You should go and turn the lights off as soon as an opportunity arises. It will not take long and will prevent the battery going flat.

(b) This should be referred to your line manager. You are very busy, but the line manager should decide whether you should go – it may be possible for the line manager to delegate your work to someone else.

(c) The friend should be told politely that you cannot speak during working hours. You could suggest a lunch-time meeting.

(d) This looks like an obvious error, or even a fraud! You cannot take action yourself, but should refer the matter to your line manager to take action.

(e) The work will have to be redone as a matter of urgency. The computer will have to be restarted and the data re-input (to the extent that it has not been saved). If there are further problems, the line manager will have to be alerted and technical assistance requested.

CHAPTER 6: WORKING AS A MEMBER OF A TEAM

6.1 A team is a group of people working together to achieve defined objectives. The benefits of working in a team include: the pooling of skills and abilities of different team members, creative thinking stimulated by group discussion, motivation from working with others, the help and support provided by other team members.

6.2 The answer will depend on the circumstances involved.

6.3 A suggested six:

1 being pleasant and polite

2 being cooperative

3 listening to and respecting the opinions of others

4 asking for and providing help

5 do not backbite

6 keep confidences

6.4 The important point here is to make sure that your objection to Jake is based on issues which relate to the work itself rather than your personal reaction to him. You should:

- Observe the ways in which the other members of the team deal with him – do they also have problems? If they do not, the problem may lie with you.
- Talk the problem over with the other team members – do they think the same way?
- Talk the matter over with Jake, if you feel you are able to.

If it emerges that the problems with Jake extend to the whole team and the standard of work and workplace efficiency is being affected, there may be a case for taking the matter to a higher authority.

6.5 Jasmina's problem is one of possible sexual discrimination, although the evidence is circumstantial rather than actual. (It may be, of course, that she is hopeless at her work.) She should in the first instance talk the matter over with the line manager, stressing her wish for promotion and motivation, making it clear that she intends to carry on working if she starts a family. If the line manager cannot come up with a satisfactory explanation for keeping her where she is, she should take the matter to a Human Resources Manager (or equivalent). If she has firm evidence of sexual discrimination, she may have grounds for starting the grievance procedure.

CHAPTER 7: CPD – DEVELOPING SKILLS AND KNOWLEDGE AT WORK

7.1 The main stages, which will involve both employee and employer, and which will be recorded, are:

(a) identification of the employee's development needs in relation to knowledge and skills

(b) identification of the employee's specific objectives in relation to knowledge and skills, ie what needs to be done, and by when. These need to be SMART (see Activity 7.2)

(c) recording of specific learning activities which help the employee to achieve the objectives

(d) evaluation of the levels of success in achieving the objectives and identification of the need for further CPD development

7.2 SMART stands for **S**pecific, **M**easurable, **A**chievable, **R**ealistic and **T**imely.

SMART is important because to be effective, objectives need to be

Specific	clear and well-defined
Measurable	success must be measurable, eg an exam pass/grade or training course certificate of competence
Achievable	the employee must have the resources to achieve the objective
Realistic	the employee must realistically believe that the objective can be met
Timely	a timescale must be set and kept to

7.3 The people involved are the employer and the employee. It is an important partnership for successful career progression.The result of their discussion at the planning stage of CPD should be a mutual agreement of the objectives to be set. As the objectives are set in motion, they will jointly monitor progress and be able to identify success rates and any problem areas on which they will have to take action. At the end of the CPD process they will jointly evaluate success and be able to plan the next stage in the CPD process.

7.4 The result of this activity will depend completely on the circumstances of the student. The plan should detail all the stages of the CPD process. If in employment the student may be able to draw on a real plan. If the student is not in employment objectives should be set by the individual, with no employer being available to advise; it may be in this case that the tutor could be asked to help the student work out a suitable action plan.

Index

for your notes

for your notes

for your notes

for your notes

for your notes

for your notes

for your notes

for your notes

for your notes

for your notes

for your notes

for your notes

for your notes